The Pursuit of Diarmuid and Grainne

&

The Exile of the Sons of Uisliu

The Pursuit of
Diarmuid and Grainne
Toruigheacht Dhiarmuda agus Ghrainne

Translated
by Standish O'Grady

&

The Exile of the Sons of Uisliu
Longes mac n-Uislenn

Translated
by A. H. Leahy

Modernized, with additional notes and a new
introduction by T. E. Kinsella

Old Baldy Press
2009

Published by
Old Baldy Press
Rochester, New York
2009

ISBN 978-0-9761157-4-8 (paperback)
ISBN 978-0-9761157-5-5 (electronic book)

Library of Congress Control Number: 2009908869

"If the autumn leaves were gold,
And the waves of the sea were silver,
Fionn would give it all away,
    All away."

>   Caoilty mac Ronain of Fionn's generosity

"According as you have planted the oak so bend
it yourself."

>   Oisin to his father

Contents

Illustrations

Introduction

The Pursuit of Diarmuid and Grainne, Toruigheacht Dhiarmuda agus Ghrainne in the Irish, is often described as a love story, and certainly important parts of the tale focus on the relationship between the heroic Diarmuid and the impetuous Grainne.[1] At the core of this Fenian tale, however, is the struggle for power, not love; and the love that is portrayed is intriguingly conflicted.

The tale opens with Fionn mac Cumhaill, the great fianna leader, wistful for a dead wife. When informed of an admirable beauty who could take her place, his first concern is for his honor, not for love. He fears that the father of this woman, the Ard Ri of Ireland, will rebuff his proposal. Consequently, he sends his son and nephew to solicit the match, stating that he "could better endure a refusal of marriage given to you than to myself." From the outset, Fionn is no romantic lover.

When Grainne, the object of Fionn's proposal, is asked whether she consents to the marriage, she cryptically replies to her father: "If he be a fitting son-in-law for you, why should he not be a fitting husband and mate for me?" Her father and Fionn's representatives understand this as consent, though subsequent events prove them wrong.

As the tale progresses, Grainne reveals great persuasive powers. She compels Diarmuid to elope with her, to sleep with her, to break his pledge to the Searbhan Lochlannach, and to host the feast that brings about his death. Her selection of Diarmuid over Fionn seems more calculating than starry-eyed, and her appetite for manipulation is striking. For his part, Diarmuid remains conflicted throughout much of the story, struggling to reconcile the requirements of duty and honor to Fionn with his obligation and eventual love for Grainne.

For more than a thousand years the saga of Diarmuid and Grainne has entertained audiences with crosscurrents of heroism and meanness, honor and dishonor, love and jealousy, and it has presented these qualities within the frame of a spirited adventure tale. The tale's longevity is well deserved.

Literacy in Early Ireland

Writing was introduced to Ireland along with Christianity in the fifth century. Latin was the language first written by missionaries, including St. Patrick, and presumably first taught to Irish converts who joined the church in ecclesiastical capacities. By the sixth or early seventh centuries, Irish churchmen were writing in their native language as well, employing what we now describe as Old Irish.

They recorded or translated saints' lives, Biblical stories, and religious tracts, along with a wide range of secular materials including genealogies, law tracts, dindsenchus (the lore of place names), histories, mythological stories, and heroic tales. Early scribes drew on Ireland's sophisticated oral tradition with its rich store of cultural knowledge which had been memorized and recited by generations of trained scholars, *file* (pl. *filidh*). These filidh, and later less thoroughly trained bards, are the ultimate sources for much early Irish literature.

Irish tales often group together into larger cycles of related stories. The most important cycles are the Mythological, whose protagonists are the Tuatha De Danann, near gods or magic people who live in the otherworldly *sidhe* and whose tales are set primarily among the burial mounds of the Boyne valley; the Kings cycle, which focuses on the activities of the ancient kings of Ireland; the Ulster cycle, which details the exploits of the Ulaid, the warriors of Ulster, including Conchobur, Fergus, Conall Cernach, and Cu Chulaind; and lastly the Fenian cycle, which describes the adventures of Fionn mac Cumhaill and his followers as they hunt the wild tracts of Ireland and protect its shores from human and magical invaders. Although well known, *The Pursuit of Diarmuid and Grainne* is only one of many tales that make up this cycle.

The Fenian Cycle

The Fenian cycle seems to have taken first shape in north Leinster, perhaps between A.D. 400 – 700.[2] Tales of Fionn and his followers were popular and spread rapidly throughout Ireland and northern Scotland. In this early period tales were transmitted orally. Eoin MacNeill argues that they resonated most deeply with the lower-classes, not with chieftains and cattle lords. He also points out that the stories change their focus based on location.[3] Thus Fionn, already associated with Leinster, is the central character and hero of tales originating in and around that province; Diarmuid O'Duibhne, with a Munster genealogy, is the hero of tales originating in the southwest of Ireland; and Goll mac Morna of Connaught is more heroic and more honest than even Fionn in tales from that region. This fluidity and adaptability is a hallmark of the Fenian cycle and suggests transmission by less skilled bards or local storytellers rather than highly-trained filidh.

At some point, perhaps as late as the tenth century, the tales began to be written down. They are preserved in numerous manuscripts, partial translations, and reworkings dating from the eleventh through the nineteenth centuries. The onset of the manuscript tradition did not diminish the oral tradition; rather the two coexisted and at times reinforced one another. Within living memory, children could hear their elders recite Fenian tales that seem to have been exclusively oral. The vigor of both traditions points to the enduring popularity of the cycle.

Most of the tales center upon Fionn mac Cumhaill, the chief of a battle group called a *fian* (pl. *fianna*). In particular, he is the leader of the fian attached to the *Ard Ri*, or High King, of Ireland. Presumably every strong ri employed fianna, small bands of highly-trained warriors. The Ard Ri's, of course, was preeminent, and Fionn held authority over all the fianna of Ireland. The size of fianna is not clear, although individual bands appear to have been small. Eleanor Hull has suggested 27 warriors to one captain or chief.[4]

Historical sources bear out the existence of fianna, fighting men in pre-Norman Ireland who were charged, in the tales at least, with the defense of Ireland's borders. More prosaically they probably served as enforcers or as primitive police forces for kings. During the winter months they were quartered upon the farming class, and during the summer months they sustained themselves through hunting.[5]

Relationships between fianna and kings were tempestuous, if the tales are any indication. Who held ultimate authority, whether ri or fianna, is depicted as an open question. Fianna were composed of men who lived outside the normal social order and who maintained a separate code of conduct. To early audiences, tales of their exploits may have represented a romantic, outlaw life, attractive but beyond the reach of ordinary members of society.[6]

According to the tales, fianna members were elite warriors, nearly superhuman, and admitted into a fian only after rigorous testing.[7] In one trial an aspirant was placed in a pit dug as deep as his knees, given a shield and a short hazel staff, and then attacked by nine warriors with spears; if the man were wounded in the attack, he would not be admitted to the fian. In another trial, among many, a man ran barefoot and at full speed across a field, impaled his foot on a four-inch thorn, and plucked it from his foot without breaking stride or losing speed.

Members had injunctions placed upon them. They could not accept a dowry with a wife but had to choose her for good manners and accomplishments alone; they could not take a woman against her will; they could not refuse a man asking for valuables or food; and no one fianna member could flee before nine warriors.

Members renounced kinship in favor of the fian. This meant that kin could not seek retribution for the death of relatives within the fianna nor could anyone seek retribution from kin for deeds perpetrated by the fianna. Fian members were required to memorize the body of tales known to all filidh; they became warrior poets who carried with them the story lore of Ireland. They also had to swear an oath of loyalty and submission to the chief of the fian, a point that plays an important role in the *Pursuit*.

Historical tradition claims that Fionn lived in the 3rd century A.D.[8] As leader of the fianna, he exhibited prodigious physical abilities and magical powers. Although his lineage differs in various branches of the cycle, in each his father is Cumhaill, hero of the Galeoin, and his mother is a daughter of the sidhe, one of the magical Tuatha De Danann. A typical genealogy identifies Fionn as son of Cumhaill and Muirrenn, daughter of Tadhg, son of Nuadhu. Tadgh and Nuadhu are alternatively identified as druids or as Tuatha De Danann residing in the Sidh of Almhuin, the Hill of Allen, where Fionn would later establish his stronghold.[9] He is a member of Clan Baoisgne.

At the heart of the Fenian cycle is a clan feud that began before the birth of Fionn. When his father, Cumhaill, served as chief of the fianna, the Ard Ri Conn of the hundred battles imposed a provincial ri upon Leinster. Cumhaill, a Leinsterman himself, chose to fight to restore power to those he considered rightful successors. At the battle of Cnucha, he stood against the forces of Conn and was killed by Goll mac Morna who replaced him as chief of the fianna.

The young Fionn, born after his father's death, was raised in secrecy, and several tales describe his upbringing and youthful adventures, including the manner in which he gained foresight from the Salmon of Knowledge. When mature, Fionn is reconciled with Conn and Goll, and throughout most of his career maintains a tenuous peace between himself, the Ard Ri, and Clan Morna. To this period, when Fionn is undisputed leader of the fianna, belong the wide-ranging tales of monster killing, invasion battles, and heroic actions. The rancor of the feud persisted, however, and most of the fianna was destroyed at the battle of Gabhra in which Oisin and Oscar, son and grandson of Fionn, fought against Clan Morna and Cairbre Liffeachair, the great grandson of Conn.

Transmission

The tale of Diarmuid and Grainne is old, finding its earliest expression in the oral repertoires of filidh or bards who preserved and conveyed the cultural heritage of pre- and early-literate Ireland. Written references to other Fenian tales date from the ninth century or earlier, and a precursor to the current story, no longer extant, appears to have been known in the tenth century.

Standish O'Grady first published the version of the *Pursuit* reprinted here in 1857. An influential scholar of Irish literature, O'Grady edited the text and printed it with his English translation on facing pages. The edition was based upon two manuscripts, one written by Labhras O'Fuarain of Cooleen, near

Portlaw, county Waterford in 1780 and another by Martan O'Griobhtha of Kilrush, county Clare in 1842-43.[10]

At least forty-one manuscript copies of the *Pursuit* survive.[11] Nearly all follow the basic outlines of the story presented here, although most conclude shortly after the death of Diarmuid and do not have the resolution offered by this version, Grainne's return to Fionn. A recent editor, Nessa Ní Shéaghdha, is convinced that this ending is neither original nor standard. Douglas Hyde, however, calls it a "most characteristic conclusion" and R. A. Breatnach writes that the ending has strong support in tradition.[12] Versions that close after Diarmuid's death certainly suggest alternative readings; nevertheless, the conclusion presented here provides an intriguing, if disconcerting climax to the tale. It reinforces a theme embodied throughout – the struggle for power – and also hints at an older, regenerative role played by Grainne.

Modernization

During the past century and a half most English readers have come to the *Pursuit* through O'Grady's translation or its modernizations. Following its first publication in 1857, it was reprinted in 1880-81. It was reissued in 1884 with slight editorial changes by

Richard J. O'Duffy, and was thus reprinted several more times. Tom Peete Cross and Clark Harris Slover included O'Grady's text, with minimal modernization, in their *Ancient Irish Tales* (New York, 1936). Various twentieth-century retellings exist, and an excellent scholarly edition of the *Pursuit*, with translation, has been completed by Nessa Ní Shéaghdha for the Irish Texts Society (Dublin, 1967).

Still, O'Grady's translation remains appealing for its thoughtful and often quite literal translation of the Irish. I have modernized it yet again, revising with a light touch in an attempt to retain a sense of the original language while making the story accessible to twenty-first century readers.

The more archaic forms of personal pronouns have been modernized, for example, *thee*, *thou*, and *thine* to *you* and *your*, and verb forms have been simplified, for example, *wouldst* to *would* and *knowest* to *know*. When O'Grady's choice of diction seems outdated, I have provided substitutions, generally following translations offered by Patrick S. Dinneen in his Irish-English dictionary.

In places, I have lightened O'Grady's punctuation, although for the most part I have retained his heavy use of semicolons, believing they help to convey the characteristically Irish piling up of clauses. At the sentence level the Irish style is accretive and quite in step with the episodic nature of the storytelling it transmits. One aspect of O'Grady's translation that

I have freely changed is paragraphing, adopting a more modern division of the text. I have also freely adapted his notes and added my own.

Structure of the Story

Although the main outlines of the *Pursuit* are clear, with Fionn's betrothal to Grainne at the opening and Diarmuid's demise near the close, much of the story develops in a loosely episodic way with little or no reason for the placement of one incident before another. Some episodes, such as the recounting of Cian's worm, seem unnecessary or redundant; others are drawn from independent tales, such as the stories Diarmuid tells before his death.

The conventions that inform Fenian storytelling may seem odd to modern readers. Abrupt transitions are frequent, such as when Fionn, playing fidchell beneath the quicken tree, blurts out "With which of us is the truth . . . with me or with Oscar?" and Diarmuid, although in hiding, responds as though his presence has already been established.

Repetition and rich use of descriptive adjectives are also typical, although compared with other tales the *Pursuit* is restrained in the use of these techniques. Still, descriptions such as Diarmuid's wrestling match with Dubh-chosach are eye-catching.

Then he and Diarmuid rushed upon one another *like wrestlers, bravely, making mighty efforts, ferocious, straining their arms* and *their swollen sinews*, as if they were *two savage oxen, or two* frenzied bulls, *or two* raging lions, *or two* fearless hawks on the edge of a cliff.

Aspects of this style derive from the heavy use of alliteration in the original Irish. Consider the same passage in Irish:

Air sin do righne fein agus Diarmuid ar a cheile go *corramhail, fearamhail, feidmeach, fuil-bheartach, fearsadach, feithreamhar*; mar a bhiadh *dha dhamh dhana, no dha* tharbh buile, *no dha* leoghan cuthaigh, *no dha* sheabhac urranta ar bhruach aille.[13]

Heavy alliteration and frequent repetition may betray the oral origins of Irish storytelling. Along with a rich descriptiveness that is typical of the tales, these features have often been lamented as stylistic blemishes by earlier commentators.[14] Nonetheless, they remain integral parts of later Irish storytelling with their use both expected and enjoyed by contemporary auditors and readers.

Fenian tales also demonstrate a timelessness resulting from the frequent revision and harmonizing that the tales underwent during transmission.[15] In one example, the green Fianna of Muir n-Iocht are also named the Men of Lochlann. Lochlann is the name usually given to Vikings or Norsemen in Irish tales. The supposed date of action in the *Pursuit*, however, predates their arrival in Ireland by several hundred years. In this instance it is not clear that the men of the green Fianna should be identified as Vikings. Rather, this phrase, presumably introduced well after the origins of the tale, simply suggests an outsider or invader. Fenian tales, with their long formulations in oral and manuscript tradition, often operate without concern for historical propriety.

Grainne

Grainne (pronounced Graanya)[16] is strong-willed, resourceful, and loving, but she is also manipulative, ambitious, and selfish. At first reading she may appear to be a well-known type – the beautiful daughter of a powerful king who is pushed toward marriage with an older man. Her course of action throughout the tale, however, suggests a more complex characterization.

The daughter of the Ard Ri, Grainne has turned away every great prince, hero, and battle-champion in Erin. As the story opens, her father, Cormac, expects her to turn away Fionn, too. Strong women are a regular feature in Irish literature, and here Grainne has more power than her very powerful father.[17] She appears in control of her destiny.

The motivation behind her ambiguous response to Fionn's marriage proposal is obscure. Should it be understood as an unequivocal, if oddly worded, acceptance? Or is it ironic? Grainne surely understands the difficult history between her father and Fionn. Is she hedging because Fionn is a powerful man? Or is this just an example of her fickle nature?

If we consider that she is intelligent and calculating – she does have access to a drugged goblet – she might be using the occasion to gain access to a new set of suitors. Cormac states that Grainne has turned away Erin's princes and chieftains, but fianna members are a cultural type unto themselves. Perhaps her acceptance was a ploy not to meet Fionn but his fianna.

This seems verified by the interrogation of Daire duanach mac Morna through which she discovers the identity of each fianna member. Her eventual confession that she has loved Diarmuid from afar is surprising given that she offers herself first to Oisin, the son of Fionn, and only after his refusal to Diarmuid.

Also telling is her willingness to impose *geasa* upon Diarmuid to ensure his compliance. The concept of a *geis* (pl. *geasa*), an injunction or taboo, is found often in early Irish literature. It can be imposed upon a person, as Grainne has done to Diarmuid, or more frequently recognized as magically associated with an individual, often by a druid. When geasa are upheld, they serve as sacred, protective hedges; the person under geasa is safe from harm. When the injunction is broken, death or disaster quickly follows. Grainne uses one of the strongest cultural bonds available to ensure Diarmuid's compliance with her wishes.

Perhaps the most intriguing aspect of Grainne's character is her drive to push Diarmuid out of his chosen life in the fianna and into the life of a cattle lord. She molds him into someone far more like her father than like Fionn.

When Diarmuid and Grainne first meet Muadhan, "a young warrior seeking a lord," Grainne encourages Diarmuid to retain him, "for you can not always remain without followers." She is encouraging Diarmuid to abandon his subservient role within the fianna and to take on the role of a prosperous noble who enters into agreements with clients and followers. She is drawing him to a lifestyle more congenial to the daughter of a ri. Eventually she succeeds, for when she and Diarmuid settle down

> . . . people used to say that there was not living at the same time with him a man richer in gold and silver, in kine and cattle-herds and sheep, and who made more successful raids, than Diarmuid.

The gift of strong and weak farmers to Druime, Diarmuid and Grainne's daughter, is yet another sign of reintegration into accepted cultural norms.[18]

Diarmuid's transformation, and that of his children, appears to be complete.

Grainne is not without attractive qualities. Her emotion at seeing that Diarmuid has survived his encounters with Fionn seems genuine, as does her lament at his death and her rage toward Fionn. Readers who find her affection for Diarmuid convincing will also acknowledge the wisdom of attempting to build a life outside the fianna.

Yet her final acts are damning. How can her distribution of Diarmuid's wealth seem anything but petty or selfish? Diarmuid's arms she bestows upon her sons but his riches she keeps to herself:

> "I myself will have the goblets, and the drinking horns, and the beautiful golden-chased cups, and the kine and the cattle-herds undivided."

It seems ironic, then, that when the sons make peace with Fionn they do so at their mother's request and by doing so gain their father's position in the fianna. Grainne took Diarmuid from the life of the fianna and fashioned with him the life of a queen, but she failed to keep her sons from following their father's first choice in life.

DIARMUID AND GRAINNE

Fionn mac Cumhaill

From the outset of this story Fionn mac Cumhaill is depicted in decline. Older and afraid of rejection, he nevertheless makes decisions that turn his followers against him. If the audience does not quickly understand that Fionn has somehow lost the respect and support of the fianna, his need for 400 mercenaries at Doire dha bhoth and the quicken tree makes this clear. With loyal followers, mercenaries are unnecessary.

Deirdre of Duibh-shleibhe, Fionn's woman messenger, expresses concern that Fionn is not strong enough to redress the wrongs done to her.

> "I have great and evil tidings to tell you, and methinks I am one without a lord."

Fionn's growing impotence is clear.

His insistence on obtaining a blood price, or *eric*, for his father from warriors who were not born at the time of his death suggests that Fionn has grown unreasonable. Certainly, Oisin and Oscar believe this, arguing that the death of the warriors' fathers at Fionn's hand should have sufficed. Fionn, however, is adamant; he will not forgive easily.

Not surprising then is Fionn's reaction upon finding Diarmuid and Grainne missing on the morning after the feast at Teamhair: "a burning jealousy and faintheartedness seized upon Fionn." He has been denied the woman that was promised and dishonored by his sworn lieutenant. It is not the fruitless chase that bothers Fionn most or even the fact that Diarmuid gives three kisses to Grainne in front of the fianna:

> "It grieves me more that the seven battalions of the standing Fianna and all the men of Erin should have witnessed you the night you took Grainne from Teamhair, seeing that you were my guard that night."

Fionn asserts that the dispute is honor-based, but it is an honor tinged with jealousy, as his comments to the dying Diarmuid make plain:

> "It likes me well to see you in that plight, O Diarmuid," said Fionn; "and I grieve that all the women of Erin are not now gazing upon you: for your excellent beauty is turned to ugliness, and your choice form to deformity."

Payback preoccupies Fionn. Even when Diarmuid nears death and asks for water, Fionn cannot see beyond the loss of Grainne:

> Fionn went for the water a second time, and he had not come more than the same distance when he let it through his hands, having thought upon Grainne.

It is fitting that at the close of the tale Fionn is filled with "hatred and great fear" for Diarmuid's children who have vowed to seek vengeance for the death of their father. Fionn is alone, having spent much of the tale breaking the bonds that hold the fianna together. Oisin remarks: "According as you have planted the oak so bend it yourself." But Fionn Mac Cumhaill, even in decline, is resourceful. In the final twist of this tale, he is able to woo Grainne successfully with "sweet words and with gentle loving discourse." He may not have won her heart at first, but he manages it at last so that "he had the desire of his heart and soul of her."

Diarmuid

Diarmuid is the most sympathetic of the three major characters. He is a highly skilled warrior and a well-liked and much valued member of the fianna. His genealogy and the direction of his flight – into the southwest of Ireland – suggest his mythic roots in Munster. He is also famed for his love spot, an indeterminate facial feature, perhaps a dimple or a birthmark (O'Grady has translated the Irish *ballach* as "freckled), that makes him irresistible to women.[19]

He is deeply committed to the fianna, asking advice from his brethren on how to handle the geasa imposed by Grainne, and readily accepting their counsel. He is unwilling to endanger any of them at Doire dha bhoth, but rather exits at the door held by Fionn. He is also unwilling to carry Grainne or anyone for any reason. The fellows of his code carry their own weight.

It is thus intriguing and somewhat sad to see him compelled to abandon the egalitarian life of the fian at the behest of Grainne. First he is implored to enter into a lord and client agreement with Muadhan (who *is* willing to carry Grainne). Next he is forced to choose between keeping trust with Fionn and enduring the taunts of Grainne.

For a considerable time during their flight, Diarmuid abstains from sex with Grainne, instead leaving signs for the pursuing fianna that show she remains untouched. In a passage that O'Grady declined to translate, although he left the Irish intact, Grainne finally expresses her frustration, suggesting that a splash of water has been more intrepid than Diarmuid.

Diarmuid's reaction is immediate.

"That is true, Grainne," said Diarmuid. "Although I have long kept myself from you out of fear of Fionn, I will not suffer myself to be reproached by you any longer; but it is difficult to give trust to a woman." Then and there it was that for the first time Diarmuid O'Duibhne did make a wife of the daughter of the Ri of Ireland, and he bore her with him into the forest.

When faced with a direct challenge to the 1 code – maintaining loyalty to Fionn or redire ⌐o that loyalty, and his love, to Grainne – he chooses the latter, although he acknowledges the difficulty of the choice.

Diarmuid indeed comes to love Grainne. The progress of his affection is marked by instructions to Aonghus who is first advised, in the event of his death, to send Grainne to her father, "and let him treat her well or ill." Later the comment softens: "whatever children Grainne may have rear and bring them up well, and send Grainne to her own father at Teamhair." His remark upon facing the wild boar of Beann Gulbain is also convincing: "Woe to him that heeds not the counsel of a good wife." Diarmuid has come to care for his mate. Still, it is a complex love. As Fionn stands over the wounded Diarmuid and charges him with dishonor, Diarmuid replies:

> "The guilt of that was not mine, O Fionn . . . Grainne put a geis upon me, and I would not have failed to keep my geasa for the gold of the world, and nothing, O Fionn, is true of all that you say."

In his denial he indicts the woman he loves.

Oisin, Oscar, and Aonghus

Providing relief for the complex characterizations of Diarmuid, Grainne, and Fionn are the simpler and perhaps more noble characters of Oisin, Oscar, and Aonghus. Oisin and Oscar, son and grandson of Fionn, have taken the code of the fianna to heart and are not willing to support their famous relative when they judge him to be wrong. Aonghus, a figure borrowed from the Mythological cycle, is a member of the magical Tuatha De Danann who provides aid on several occasions. He is foster-father to Diarmuid, and as such holds intense affection for him. As irresistible as Grainne is to others, she has no power over Aonghus.

Subtlety of the Tale

Despite the seemingly haphazard and episodic nature of this tale, many scenes set forth surprisingly careful evocations of character. One that showcases Diarmuid's relationship with both Grainne and Fionn takes place as the couple lie atop the quicken tree. The exchange suggests the complexity of ties among the characters.

Fionn has arrived at the tree certain that Diarmuid has slain its guardian and that he remains at the top of the tree. Oisin chides his father: "It is a great sign of envy in you, O Fionn, to suppose that Diarmuid would abide in the top of the quicken tree, and he knowing that you are intent on slaying him." Fionn, perhaps because of his magical foresight, is resolute and does not stir. Instead he challenges Oisin to a game of fidchell, a board game like chess.

With Fionn on one side of the board and his son, close relatives, and friends on the other, the lonely position of Fionn is made clear. Still, he plays with enough skill to all but defeat Oisin. Up in the tree, Diarmuid follows the game and laments his inability to show the winning move. Grainne chides him, suggesting that it is worse for him to be stuck at the top of the tree "with the seven battalions of the standing Fianna round about you intent upon your destruction, than that Oisin should lack that move." Despite this reasonable comment, Diarmuid repeatedly throws well-aimed berries that not only reveal the correct move but also his presence and that of Grainne. His impulse is to assist his fian mate, not to protect the pregnant Grainne.

Another stark interplay of character occurs after Diarmuid's death when Fionn walks to Rath Ghrainne with Diarmuid's favorite hound in hand. Grainne asks to be given the dog, but Fionn refuses, retorting that he thought it not too much to inherit the favorite hound of Diarmuid. Oisin's response, to quietly take the dog from Fionn and hand it to Grainne, is telling.

Finally, there is the difficult scene at the heart of the tale where Diarmuid and Grainne, fleeing from the men of the green fianna, find the pursuers close behind. Diarmuid becomes enraged at the sight of them, especially at the youth in the forefront of the company. He had previously given his dagger to Grainne so that she might trim her nails. At this critical juncture, she "reached the dagger to Diarmuid" who "thrust it upon his thigh." He then makes a baffling comment: "I trust you bear the youth of the green mantle no love, Grainne." Her response is equally out of place: "Truly I do not . . . and I would I never to this day had borne love to any."

Clearly sparks have flown between the couple, although the reason is not apparent. This dramatic scene only comes into sharper focus with the knowledge that other versions of the tale exist in which Grainne indeed has an affair with a stranger, presumably the figure of the green youth in our tale.[20]

The absence of this crucial information may be due to corruptions in the manuscript tradition or, more likely, to a storyteller or scribe who at some point in the transmission felt that certain details lessened the decorum of the tale. The break highlights the communal nature of the *Pursuit*. This tale is not the work of one author at one time but of many storytellers over many generations. It is not a window into some ancient past, but rather an artful presentation of cultural belief that, passing through time, has remained recognizable to both storytellers and audiences.

For modern readers, and I argue for many earlier auditors as well, *The Pursuit of Diarmuid and Grainne* gains its power from the fidelity with which it presents the human condition. Its relationships are memorable; characters have familar motivations; and emotions are depicted with harsh honesty. Despite the archaic trappings of the story this is a familiar and touching world.

T. E. Kinsella
Perth, Ontario

Notes

Many people have made this text possible. I am indebted foremost to Standish O'Grady and A. H. Leahy whose work is here modernized. Thanks also go to the students who have read Irish literature with me over the years; they have taught me to appreciate the new along with the old. I am grateful to Jaime Bertoti and Rhonda L. Llanos for their comments on early drafts and to the staff of the Stockton library who have been efficient and helpful as always.

∾

[1] Myles Dillon describes the *Pursuit* as "the tragedy of a young girl betrothed to an old man and of the conflict between passion and duty on the part of her lover. In . . . [this] case death is the price of love"; *Early Irish Literature* (Chicago: University of Chicago Press, 1948) 42-43. R. A. Breatnach describes the story thusly: "Here is a theme that manifestly belongs to great literature: the story of a tragic love, set in a milieu of primeval nature touched with 'that magic of Celtic romance, which Matthew Arnold loved and praised,' and elaborated in a peculiar, original style of story-telling redolent of antiquity"; "The Pursuit of Diarmaid and Gráinne," *Studies: An Irish Quarterly Review* 47 (1958) 90. Eleanor Hull describes the subject of the tale as love in *A Text Book of Irish Literature*, pt. 2 (Dublin: M. H. Gill & Son, Ltd., n.d.) 53.

[2] Eoin MacNeill, *Duanaire Finn: The Book of the Lays of Fionn*, pt. 1 (London: The Irish Texts Society, 1908) xxxvi.

[3] MacNeill xxiv-xliii. Gerard Murphy is in basic agreement with MacNeill on these points in *The Ossianic Lore and Romantic Tales of Medieval Ireland* (Dublin: The Cultural Relations Committee of Ireland, 1961).

[4] Hull, *Text Book* 6. Geoffrey Keating suggests different numbers

with the fianna employing ranks of officers similar to colonel, captain, lieutenant, and corporal in the modern armed forces; *The History of Ireland* (London: The Irish Texts Society, 1902-14) sec. xlv, 333.

[5] For more historical details of the fianna see Kuno Meyer, *Fianaigecht*, Royal Irish Academy Todd Lecture Series, vol. XVI (Dublin: Hodges, Figgis & Co., Ltd., 1910; reprinted 1937) and Kim McCone, *Pagan Past and Christian Present in Early Irish Literature* (Maynooth: an Sagart, 1990).

[6] Nerys Patterson, *Cattle Lords & Clansmen: The Social Structure of Early Ireland* (Notre Dame: University of Notre Dame Press, 1994) 47.

[7] For a lengthier description of these tests, injunctions, and conditions, see Keating, *The History of Ireland* sec. xlv, 333-35.

[8] Fionn's death has been identified in A.D. 252, 283 or 286. Hull, *Text Book* 4.

[9] For more see MacNeill xlv and lii-lv.

[10] Standish O'Grady, ed., *Toruigheacht Dhiarmuda agus Ghrainne; or, The Pursuit After Diarmuid O'Duibhne, and Grainne the Daughter of Cormac Mac Airt, King of Ireland in the Third Century* (Dublin: The Ossianic Society, 1857). See pages 30-31 for O'Grady's discussion of these manuscripts. According to Nessa Ní Shéaghdha, the 1842-43 manuscript can no longer be found, and only a second copy of the 1780 manuscript survives; Shéaghdha, *Tóruigheacht Dhiarmada agus Ghráinne: The Pursuit of Diarmaid and Gráinne* (Dublin: The Irish Texts Society, 1967) xv.

[11] Shéaghdha xiv.

[12] Shéaghdha xvii-xviii; Douglas Hyde, *A Literary History of Ireland* (London: Ernest Benn, 1980) 385, n. 1; Breatnach 92.

[13] O'Grady 94.

[14] Attempting to compliment the style of the *Pursuit*, Eleanor Hull writes: "The tale is told with much simplicity and with none of the long adjectival passages which deface a portion of Irish prose romance"; *Text Book* 53.

[15] MacNeill discusses a note in the Book of Leinster appended to the list of stories filidh were required to memorize: "He is no fili who does not harmonize and synchronize all the stories." To MacNeill this is proof that filidh were able, indeed required to update the overall cohesiveness of story cycles. MacNeill xxxix.

[16] Hyde 395.

[17] In her power over her father, Grainne is comparable to Caer in the mythological tale "Dream of Oengus"; Caer's father admits "Her power is greater than mine"; Jeffrey Gantz, *Early Irish Myths and Sagas* (London: Penguin, 1981) 111. Irish literature is well populated by strong women, including Emer, Fand, Macha, Maeve, and of course Deirdre, the protagonist of *The Exile of the Sons of Uisliu*.

[18] See p. 133 within the text.

[19] In other tales, Diarmuid's love spot is described on his forehead or shoulder and usually covered. In some variants of this tale, Grainne sees the love spot uncovered during the fateful hurling match and thus falls hopelessly in love.

[20] Shéaghdha xxiii.

Brugh na Boyne

Gabhra

Teamhair

Eamhuin
(Emain Macha)

Sidh Fionnachaidh

Sliabh Guaire

Eas Ruaidh
mhic Bhadhairn

Rath Ghráinne
Céis
Coraill

Beann Gulbain

R. Muaidh Sliabh
(Moy) Lugha

Uí Fhiachrach
Muaidh

Sliabh Mor

Ireland in the time

Beinn Etair

Beann Damhuis

Magh
Bhreagh Cnucha

Almhuin

Beul
atha luain

R. Sioma

Sliabh Crot

Sliabh Cua

Doire dha both

Sliabh Echtghe

Ros da shoileach
(Luimneach)

Cnoc Áine

Sliabh Muice

Ui Fhidhrach

Aidhne

Cnoc na n-os

Uí Chonaill
Gabhra

Sliabh
Luachra

Ciarraidhe
Luachra

Teamhair
Luachra

R. Fionliath

Sliabh Mis

R. Leamhain

R. Caol

R. Éin

R. Fleisge

Corca Ui Dhuibhne

Currach cinn admuid
(Tonn Toime)

of the *Pursuit*

The Pursuit

Glossary

Alba. Northern Scotland.

Ard Ri. High King.

Ath. A ford.

Brugh. A large house, palace or fort; the abode of one of the Tuatha De Danann; a hillock or mound (believed to be the abode of the Tuatha De Danann).

Brugh na Boyne. The Brugh of the Boyne. Newgrange in the Boyne river valley.

Drom. A back, a ridge.

Dun. A fort or fortress, a royal residence or fortified mansion.

Ga. A javelin or small spear.

Geis (pl. *geasa*). A solemn injunction, especially of a magical kind, the breaking of which led to misfortune and even death.

Mag. A plain. A field or level district.

Mor. Big, great, large, extensive.

Rath. A rath is a circular compound, including house, outbuildings, and enclosing wall, common to the Irish warrior class.

Ri (pl. *rioga*). A king or ruler; the principal person of a group.

Sidhe. The magical otherworld populated by the Tuatha De Danann. The entrance to the sidhe was through burial mounds, the most famous of which is the Brugh na Boyne.

Sliabh. A mountain, range of mountains, or mountainous district.

Tuatha De Danann. Protagonists of the Mythological cycle. Near gods or magic people who live in the otherworldly *sidhe* and whose tales are set primarily among the burial mounds of the Boyne valley.

The Pursuit of
Diarmuid and Grainne

On a certain day when Fionn mac Cumhaill rose at early morn in Almhuin,[1] in Leinster, and sat upon the grass-green plain, having neither servant nor attendant with him, there followed him two of his people; that is, Oisin the son of Fionn, and Diorruing the son of Dobhar O'Baoisgne.[2]

Oisin spoke, and what he said was, "What is the cause of this early rising of yours, O Fionn?"

"Not without cause have I made this early rising," said Fionn; "for I am without a wife since Maignes the daughter of Garad Glundub mac Moirne died; for he is not wont to have slumber nor sweet sleep who happens to be without a fitting wife, and that is the cause of my early rising, O Oisin."

"What forces you to be thus?" said Oisin; "for there is not a wife nor a mate in the green-landed island of Erin upon whom you might turn the light of your

∽

[1] *Almhuin* is the Hill of Allen in county Kildare. Tradition names it as the site of Fionn's stronghold.

[2] *O'Baoisgne* translates as descendant of Baoisgne. The namesake of Clan Baoisgne was Fionn's grandfather (according to one genealogy) or his great, great, great grandfather (according to another). Fionn, his son Oisin, and Diorruing are all members of the clan Baoisgne.

eyes or of your sight, whom we would not bring by fair means or by foul to you."

And then spoke Diorruing, and what he said was, "I myself could discover for you a wife and a fitting mate."

"Who is she?" said Fionn.

"She is Grainne the daughter of Cormac, the son of Art, the son of Conn of the hundred battles," said Diorruing, "that is, the woman that is fairest of feature and form and speech of the women of the globe together."

"Truthfully, O Diorruing," said Fionn, "there has been strife and variance between Cormac and myself for a long time,[1] and I think it not good nor seemly that he should give me a refusal of marriage; and I had rather that you should both go to ask the hand of his daughter for me of Cormac, for I could better endure a refusal of marriage given to you than to myself."

"We will go there," said Oisin, "though there be no profit for us there, and let no man know of our journey until we come back again."

∽

[1] The trouble began between Fionn's father, Cumhaill, and Cormac's grandfather, Conn. Conn had slain Cathair Mor, a high king of Ireland from Leinster, and at the battle of Cnucha (now Castleknock in county Dublin) Cumhaill, the chief of the Fianna of Ireland, fought Conn to restore power to the descendants of Cathair Mor. Cumhaill was killed in that battle by Goll mac Morna. Enmity between Fionn and Cormac and Fionn and Clan Morna was thus born.

After that, those two good warriors went their way, and they took farewell of Fionn, and it is not told how they fared until they reached Teamhair.[2] The Ri[3] of Erin chanced to be holding a gathering and a muster before them upon the plain of Teamhair, and the chiefs and the great nobles of his people were with him. A friendly welcome was given to Oisin and Diorruing, and the gathering was then put off until another day, for the Ri was certain that it was upon some pressing matter that those two had come to him. Afterwards Oisin called the Ri of Erin to one side, and told him that it was to ask of him the marriage of his daughter for Fionn mac Cumhaill that they were then come.

Cormac spoke, and what he said was, "There is not a son of a ri or of a great prince, a hero or a battle-champion in Erin, to whom my daughter has not given refusal of marriage, and it is on me that all and everyone lays the blame for that; so I will not give you any formal decision until you go yourselves to my daughter, for it is better that you hear her own

∽

[2] According to tradition *Teamhair,* modernized Tara, is the seat of the *ard ri,* or high king, of Ireland, thus the proper abode for Cormac. The Hill of Tara is located near the River Boyne in county Meath. Archeological studies have identified neolithic and iron age structures on the hill, suggesting its cultural significance and great antiquity.

[3] *Ri* (pl. *rioga*) is the Irish term for king. Although details are complex, Irish rioga were normally elected; they did not inherit the position.

45

words than that you be displeased with me."

After that they went their way to the grianan,[1] and Cormac sat upon the side of the couch and of the high bed by Grainne, and he said, "Here, O Grainne, are two of the people of Fionn mac Cumhaill coming to ask you as wife and as mate for him, and what answer would you give them?"

Grainne answered, and what she said was, "If he be a fitting son-in-law for you, why should he not be a fitting husband and mate for me?"

Then they were satisfied; and after that a feast and banquet was made for them in the bower with Grainne and the women, so that they became intoxicated and mirthful; and Cormac appointed a meeting with them and with Fionn a fortnight from that night at Teamhair.

Thereafter Oisin and Diorruing arrived again at Almhuin, where they found Fionn and the Fianna, and they told them their news from beginning to end.

Now as everything wears away, so also did that space of time; and then Fionn collected and assembled the seven battalions[2] of the standing Fianna

~

[1] A *grianan* is a sun porch or sunny place within a dwelling, a solarium. O'Grady translates *grianan* as "the dwelling of the women"; Eleanor Hull in *A Text Book of Irish Literature* glosses *grianan* as "women's house" (54).

[2] Each battalion of the Fianna was supposed to have 3,000 men (Keating, sec. xlv, 331).

from every quarter where they were, and they came where Fionn was, in Almhuin the great and broad of Leinster; and on the last day of that period of time they went forth in great bands, in troops, and in impetuous fierce impenetrable companies, and we are not told how they fared until they reached Teamhair.

Cormac was before them upon the plain with the chiefs and the great nobles of the men of Erin about him, and they made a gentle welcome for Fionn and all the Fianna, and after that they went to the Ri's festive house called Midcuart. The Ri of Erin sat down to enjoy drinking and pleasure with his wife at his left shoulder, that is, Eitche, the daughter of Atan of Corcaigh, and Grainne at her shoulder, and Fionn mac Cumhaill at the Ri's right hand; and Cairbre Liffeachair the son of Cormac sat at one side of the same royal house, and Oisin the son of Fionn at the other side, and each one of them sat according to his rank and to his patrimony from there down.

A druid and a skillful man of knowledge of the people of Fionn sat before Grainne the daughter of Cormac; that is, Daire duanach[3] mac Morna; and it was not long before gentle conversation and dialogue arose between him and Grainne. Then Daire duanach mac Morna arose and stood before Grainne, and sang her the songs and the verses and the sweet poems of

∾

[3] *Daire duanach* translates as Daire the poetic or Daire of the poems.

her fathers and of her ancestors.

Then Grainne spoke and asked the druid, "What is the reason why Fionn is come to this place tonight?"

"If you do not know that," said the druid, "it is no wonder that I know it not."

"I desire to learn it of you," said Grainne.

"Well then," said the druid, "it is to ask you as wife and as mate that Fionn is come to this place tonight."

"It is a great marvel to me," said Grainne, "that it is not for Oisin that Fionn asks me, for it were fitter to give me such as he, than a man that is older than my father."

"Say not that," said the druid, "for were Fionn to hear you he himself would not have you, neither would Oisin dare to take you."

"Tell me now," said Grainne, "who is that warrior at the right shoulder of Oisin the son of Fionn?"

"That," said the druid, "is Goll mac Morna, the active, the warlike."

"Who is that warrior at the shoulder of Goll?" said Grainne.

"Oscar the son of Oisin," said the druid.

"Who is that graceful-legged man at the shoulder of Oscar?" said Grainne.

"Caoilte mac Ronain," said the druid.

"What haughty impetuous warrior is that beyond the shoulder of Caoilte?" said Grainne.

"The son of Lughaidh of the mighty hand, and that man is sister's son to Fionn mac Cumhaill," said the druid.[1]

"Who is that freckled sweet-worded man, upon whom is the curling dusky-black hair and the two red ruddy cheeks, upon the left hand of Oisin the son of Fionn?"[2]

"That man is Diarmuid the grandson of Duibhne, the white-toothed, of the lightsome countenance; that is, the best lover of women and of maidens in the whole world."

"Who is that at the shoulder of Diarmuid?" said Grainne.

"Diorruing the son of Dobhar Damhadh O'Baois-gne, and that man is a druid and a skillful man of science," said Daire duanach.

"That is a goodly company," said Grainne; and she called her attendant handmaid to her, and told her to bring to her the jewelled golden-chased goblet which was in the grianan behind her. The handmaid brought the goblet, and Grainne filled the goblet immediately, and it contained the drink of nine times nine men.

∾

[1] The *sister's son*, a nephew by one's sister, is an especially significant familial relationship often noted in early Irish literature. Its importance may be evidence of earlier matrilineal patterns of descent.

[2] The Irish *ballach* is here translated "freckled," but almost certainly refers to Diarmuid O'Duibhne's "love spot," a freckle, dimple, or mole that made him irresistible to women.

Grainne said, "Take the goblet to Fionn first, and bid him drink a draught out of it, and disclose to him that it is I that sent it to him."

The handmaid took the goblet to Fionn, and told him everything that Grainne had bid her say to him. Fionn took the goblet, and no sooner had he drunk a draught out of it than there fell upon him a stupor of sleep and of deep slumber. Cormac took the draught and the same sleep fell upon him, and Eitche, the wife of Cormac, took the goblet and drank a draught out of it, and the same sleep fell upon her as upon all the others.

Then Grainne called the attendant handmaid to her, and said to her: "Take this goblet to Cairbre Lifeachair and tell him to drink a draught out of it, and give the goblet to those sons of rioga by him."[1]

The handmaid took the goblet to Cairbre, and he was not well able to give it to him who sat next to him before a stupor of sleep and of deep slumber fell upon him too, and each one that took the goblet, one after another, fell into a stupor of sleep and of deep slumber.

When Grainne saw that they were in a state of drunkenness and of trance, she rose fairly and softly from the seat on which she was, and spoke to Oisin, and what she said was, "I marvel at Fionn mac

⁓

[1] *Rioga* (pl. of *ri*), kings. These are the followers of Cormac, not of Fionn.

Cumhaill that he should seek such a wife as I, for it were fitter for him to give me my own equal to marry than a man older than my father."

"Say not that, O Grainne," said Oisin, "for if Fionn were to hear you he would not have you, neither would I dare to take you."

"Will you receive courtship from me, O Oisin?" said Grainne.

"I will not," said Oisin, "for whatever woman is betrothed to Fionn, I would not meddle with her."

Then Grainne turned her face to Diarmuid O'Duibhne, and what she said to him was, "Will you receive courtship from me, O son of O'Duibhne, since Oisin receives it not from me?"

"I will not," said Diarmuid, "for whatever woman is betrothed to Oisin I may not take her, even were she not betrothed to Fionn."

"Then," said Grainne, "I put you under geasa[2] of danger and of destruction, O Diarmuid, that is, under the geasa of dread and vengeance, if you take me not with you out of this household tonight before Fionn and the Ri of Erin arise out of that sleep."

❧

[2] A *geis* (pl. *geasa*) is an injunction, bond, or taboo. It can be imposed upon a person, as Grainne has done to Diarmuid, or recognized as associated with an individual, often by a druid. When geasa are upheld, they appear to serve as sacred, protective hedges; if they remain unbroken, the person under geasa is safe from harm. When the injunction is broken, death or disaster quickly follows.

"Evil are those geasa under which you have laid me, O woman," said Diarmuid. "Why have you laid those geasa upon me in preference to all the sons of rioga and of high princes in the Ri's festive house called Midcuart this night, seeing that there is not of all those one less worthy to be loved by a woman than myself?"

"By your hand, O son of O'Duibhne, it is not without cause that I have laid those geasa on you, as I will tell you now. One day when the Ri of Erin was presiding over a gathering and muster on the plain of Teamhair, Fionn and the seven battalions of the standing Fianna chanced to be there that day; and there arose a great hurling[1] match between Cairbre Liffeachair the son of Cormac and Mac Lughaidh. The men of Breagha, and Cerna, and the stout pillars of Teamhair arose on the side of Cairbre, and the Fianna of Erin on the side of Mac Lughaidh; and there were none sitting in the gathering that day but the Ri, and Fionn, and yourself, O Diarmuid. It happened that the game was going against the son of Lughaidh, and you rose and stood, and took the hurley stick from the man near to you, and threw him

∾

[1] Hurling is an ancient sport played in Ireland to this day. Players use sticks, or hurleys, similar to field hockey sticks but with flattened blades, to strike a small ball into or above a goal. Tales in the Ulster Cycle often mention "boys troops" playing aggressive games of hurley, presumably excellent practice for battle.

to the ground and to the earth, and you went into the game, and won the goal three times upon Cairbre and upon the warriors of Teamhair. I was at that time in my grianan of the clear view, of the blue windows of glass, gazing upon you, and I turned the light of my eyes and of my sight upon you that day, and I never gave that love to any other man from that time to this, and will not forever."

"It is a wonder that you should give me that love instead of Fionn," said Diarmuid, "seeing that there is not in Erin a man who is fonder of a woman than he; and do you know, O Grainne, on the night that Fionn is in Teamhair that it is he that has the keys of Teamhair, and because of that we cannot depart from this place?"

"There is a door of elopement out of my grianan," said Grainne, "and we will pass out through it."

"It is a geis for me to pass through any escape door whatsoever," said Diarmuid.

"Nevertheless, I hear," said Grainne, "that every warrior and battle-champion can pass by the shafts of his javelins and by the staves of his spears, in or out over the rampart of every fort and of every stronghold. I will pass out by the door, and do you follow me in that way."

Grainne went her way out, and Diarmuid spoke to his people, and what he said was, "O Oisin, son of Fionn, what shall I do with this geis that has been laid on me?"

"You are not guilty of the geis which has been laid upon you," said Oisin, "and I tell you to follow Grainne, and keep yourself well against the wiles of Fionn."

"O Oscar, son of Oisin, what is good for me to do as to those geasa which have been laid upon me?"

"I tell you to follow Grainne," said Oscar, "for he is a wretched man that fails to keep his geasa."

"What counsel do you give me, O Caoilte?" said Diarmuid.

"I say," said Caoilte, "that I have a fitting wife, and yet I had rather than the wealth of the world that it had been to me that Grainne gave that love."

"What counsel do you give me, O Diorruing?"

"I tell you to follow Grainne, though your death will come of it, and I grieve for it."

"Is that the counsel of you all to me?" said Diarmuid.

"It is," said Oisin, and said all the others together.

After that Diarmuid arose and stood, and stretched forth his active warrior hand over his broad weapons, and took leave and farewell of Oisin and of the chiefs of the Fianna; and not bigger is a smooth-crimson whortleberry than was each tear that Diarmuid shed from his eyes at parting with his people.[1]

Diarmuid went to the top of the fort, and put the

❦

[1] The whortleberry, also known as bilberry, is a low shrub found on heaths and in woods, usually at higher elevations. The black or dark blue fruit is tart and similar in appearance to a blueberry, though somewhat smaller.

shafts of his two javelins under him, and rose with an airy, very light, exceeding high, bird-like leap, until he landed on the two soles of his feet on the beautiful grass-green earth of the plain outside, and Grainne met him.

Then Diarmuid spoke, and what he said was, "I believe, O Grainne, that this is an evil course upon which you are come; for it were better for you to have Fionn mac Cumhaill for a lover than myself, seeing that I know not what nook or corner, or remote part of Erin I can take you to now, and return again to this place, without Fionn's learning what you have done."

"It is certain that I will not go back," said Grainne, "and that I will not part from you until death part me from you."

"Then go forward, O Grainne," said Diarmuid.

Diarmuid and Grainne went their way after that, and they had not gone beyond a mile from Teamhair when Grainne said, "Indeed I am wearying, O son of O'Duibhne."

"It is a good time to weary, O Grainne," said Diarmuid, "and return now to your own household again, for I give you the word of a true warrior that I will never carry you, nor any other woman, to all eternity."

"You need not do so," said Grainne, "for my father's horses are in a fenced meadow by themselves, and they have chariots. Return you to them, and yoke two horses of them to a chariot, and I will wait for you on this spot till you overtake me again."

Diarmuid returned to the horses, and he yoked two horses of them to a chariot. It is not told how Diarmuid and Grainne fared until they reached Beul atha luain.[1]

Then Diarmuid spoke to Grainne, and said, "It is all the easier for Fionn to follow our track, O Grainne, because we have the horses."

"Then," said Grainne, "leave the horses upon this spot, and henceforth I will journey on foot by you."

Diarmuid got down at the edge of the ford, and took a horse with him over across the ford, and thus left one of them upon each side of the stream, and he and Grainne went a mile with the stream westward, and went on land at the side of the province of Connacht. It is not told how they fared until they arrived at Doire dha bhoth, in the midst of Clanna Riocaird[2]; and Diarmuid cut down the grove around him, and made to it seven doors of wattles,[3] and he settled a bed of soft rushes and of the tops of the birch under Grainne in the very midst of that wood.

~

[1] *Beul atha luain* is the mouth of the ford of Luan, now Athlone.
[2] *Doire dha bhoth* translates as the grove of the two huts. It is in Clanrickard, a territory that comprised six baronies in county Galway: Leitrim, Loughreagh, Dunkellin, Kiltartan, Clare and Athenry.
[3] *Wattle* is a form of weaving that is similar but more robust than wicker. Poles or stakes are interlaced with flexible branches or twigs, weaving a strong fence, wall, or in this case door.

As for Fionn mac Cumhaill, I will tell his tidings clearly. All who were in Teamhair rose at early morn the next day, and they found Diarmuid and Grainne wanting from among them, and a burning jealousy and faintheartedness seized upon Fionn. He found his trackers before him on the plain, that is the Clanna Neamhuin, and he bade them follow Diarmuid and Grainne. Then they carried the track as far as Beul atha luain, and Fionn and the Fianna of Erin followed them; but they could not find the track over across the ford, so that Fionn pledged his word that if they found not the track speedily, he would hang them on either side of the ford.

Then the Clanna Neamhuin went upstream, and found a horse on either side of the stream; and they went a mile with the stream westward, and found the track by the side of the province of Connacht, and Fionn and the Fianna of Erin followed them. Then spoke Fionn, and what he said was, "Well I know where Diarmuid and Grainne shall be found now, that is in Doire dha bhoth."

Oisin, and Oscar, and Caoilte, and Diorruing, the son of Dobhar Damhadh O'Baoisgne, were listening to Fionn speaking these words, and Oisin spoke, and what he said was, "We are in danger lest Diarmuid and Grainne be at this place, and we must send him some warning. Find where Bran is, that is, the hound of Fionn mac Cumhaill, that we may send him to Diarmuid, for Fionn himself is not dearer to him than Diarmuid is; and, O Oscar, tell Bran to go with a warning to Diarmuid, who is in Doire dha bhoth"; and Oscar told that to Bran.[1]

Bran understood with knowledge and wisdom, and went back to the rear of the host where Fionn might not see him, and followed Diarmuid and Grainne by their track until he reached Doire dha bhoth, and thrust his head into Diarmuid's bosom as he slept.

Then Diarmuid sprang out of his sleep, and awoke Grainne also, and said to her: "Here is Bran, the hound of Fionn mac Cumhaill, coming with a warning to us before Fionn himself."

"Take that warning," said Grainne, "and fly."

"I will not take it," said Diarmuid, "for I would not that Fionn caught me at any other time rather than now, since I may not escape from him."[2] When Grainne heard this, dread and great fear seized her, and Bran departed from them.

෴

[1] Bran was one of Fionn's two prize hounds; the other was Sceolan. Bran and Sceolan were intelligent with some human qualities, not surprising since they were born to Fionn's aunt, who had been transformed by a jealous lady of the sidhe into a dog. For an informative article available through *JSTOR*, see Reinhard, John R. and Vernam E. Hull, "Bran and Sceolang," *Speculum* 11.1 (1936) 42-58.

[2] This obscure phrasing seems to mean "I will not fly, for I would rather Fionn catch me now since escape is impossible." The sentiment may be fatalistic or perhaps heroically boastful.

Then Oisin the son of Fionn spoke and said, "We are in danger that Bran may not have had the opportunity to go to Diarmuid, and we must give him some other warning. Look where Fearghoir is, the footman of Caoilte."

"He is with me," said Caoilte. Now Fearghoir was such that every shout he gave used to be heard in the three districts nearest to him. Then they made him give three shouts, in order that Diarmuid might hear him. Diarmuid heard Fearghoir, and awoke Grainne out of her sleep, and what he said was, "I hear the footman of Caoilte mac Ronain, and he is with Caoilte, and Caoilte is with Fionn, and this is a warning they are sending me."

"Take that warning," said Grainne.

"I will not," said Diarmuid, "for we shall not leave this wood until Fionn and the Fianna of Erin overtake us"; and fear and great dread seized Grainne when she heard that.

As for Fionn, I will tell his tidings clearly. He did not abandon the chase until he reached Doire dha bhoth, and he sent the Clanna Eamhuin[3] to search out the wood, and they saw Diarmuid and a woman by him. They returned back again to Fionn and the Fianna of Erin, and Fionn asked of them whether

～

[3] *Clanna Eamhuin* translates as the race or children of Eamhuin. Eamhuin, now called in English Navan, is a well-known town in county Meath.

Diarmuid or Grainne were in the wood. "Diarmuid is there," they said, "and there is some woman by him; who she is we know not for we know Diarmuid's track, but we know not the track of Grainne."

"Foul befall the friends of Diarmuid O'Duibhne for his sake," said Fionn. "He shall not leave the wood until he gives me satisfaction for every thing he has done to me."

"It is a great token of jealousy in you, O Fionn," said Oisin, "to think that Diarmuid would stay upon the plain of Maenmhagh,[1] seeing that at that place there is no stronghold but Doire dha bhoth, and you too awaiting him."

"That shall profit you nothing, O Oisin," said Fionn, "and well I knew the three shouts that Caoilte's servant gave, that it was you who sent them as a warning to Diarmuid; and that it was you who sent my own hound, that is, Bran, with another warning to him. But it shall profit you nothing to have sent him any of those warnings; for he shall not leave Doire dha bhoth until he gives me eric[2] for everything that he has done to me, and for every slight that he has

~

[1] *Maenmhagh* was the name of a large level tract lying round Loughrea in county Galway.

[2] *Eiric,* anglicized *eric*, is a fine, ransom, or restitution given to compensate some wrong. It often refers to compensation made to relatives for unlawful murder. See p. 94 where Fionn demands eric for the death of his father.

put on me."

"Great foolishness it is for you, O Fionn," said Oscar the son of Oisin, "to suppose that Diarmuid would stay in the midst of this plain, and you waiting to take his head from him."

"Who else cut the wood thus, and made a close warm enclosure from the cuttings, with seven tight slender-narrow doors to it? And with which of us, O Diarmuid, is the truth, with myself or with Oscar?" said Fionn.

"You did never err in your good judgment, O Fionn," said Diarmuid, "and I and Grainne are indeed here." Then Fionn bade the Fianna of Erin come round Diarmuid and seize him.

Thereupon Diarmuid rose up and stood and gave Grainne three kisses in the presence of Fionn and of the Fianna, so that a burning jealousy and a faint-heartedness seized Fionn upon seeing that, and he said that Diarmuid should give his head for those kisses.

As for Aonghus of the Brugh,[3] that is, the tutor in learning of Diarmuid O'Duibhne, it was shown to

∾

[3] *Aonghus*, Diarmuid's foster father, is a member of the Tuatha De Danann, the otherworldly folk who live in the sidhe, entrance to which is gained through various sacred mounds. The site of Brugh na Boyne is Newgrange. For earlier tales about Aonghus read "The Wooing of Etain" and "The Dream of Oengus" in Gantz's *Early Irish Myths and Sagas*.

Aonghus of the Brugh

him in the Brugh na Boyne the extremity in which his foster-son, Diarmuid, then was; and he proceeded accompanying the pure-cold wind, and he halted not till he reached Doire dha bhoth. Then he went unknown to Fionn or to the Fianna of Erin to the place where Diarmuid and Grainne were, and he greeted Diarmuid, and what he said was, "What is this thing that you have done, O son of O'Duibhne?"

"This it is," said Diarmuid; "the daughter of the Ri of Erin has fled secretly with me from her father and from Fionn, and it is not by my will that she has come with me."

"Then let one of you come under either border of my mantle," said Aonghus, "and I will take you out of this place without the knowledge of Fionn or of the Fianna of Erin."

"Take Grainne with you," said Diarmuid. "As for me, I will never go with you. However, if I am alive presently I will follow you, and if I do not, do you send Grainne to her father, and let him treat her well or ill."

After that Aonghus put Grainne under the border of his mantle, and went his way without knowledge of Fionn or of the Fianna of Erin, and no tale is told of them until they reached Ros da shoileach which is now called Luimneach.[1]

After Aonghus and Grainne had departed from Diarmuid, he arose as a straight pillar and stood upright, and girded his arms and his armor and his various sharp weapons about him. After that he drew near to one of the seven doors of wattle of the enclo-

∾

[1] *Ros da shoileach* translates as the promontory of the two sallows (a type of willow). *Luimneach* was originally the name of the lower Shannon and is the site of present-day Limerick.

sure, and asked who was at it.

"No foe to you is any man who is at it," said they, "for here are Oisin the son of Fionn, and Oscar the son of Oisin, and the chieftains of the Clanna Baoisgne together with us. Come out to us, and none will dare to do you harm, hurt, or damage."

"I will not go to you," said Diarmuid, "until I see at which door Fionn himself is." He drew near to another wattled door, and asked who was at it.

"Caoilte the son of Crannachar mac Ronain, and the Clanna Ronain together with him. Come out to us and we will fight and die for your sake."

"I will not go to you," said Diarmuid, "for I will not cause Fionn to be angry with you for doing well to myself." He drew near to another wattled door, and asked who was at it.

"Here are Conan the son of Fionn of Liathluachra, and the Clanna Morna together with him; and we are enemies to Fionn, and you are far dearer to us than he, and for that reason come out to us, and none will dare meddle with you."[1]

"Surely I will not go," said Diarmuid, "for Fionn had rather the death of every man of you, than that I should be let out." He drew near to another wattled door, and asked who was there.

❧

[1] These were men of the clan Morna, fianna members of Connacht, whose feud with Fionn stemmed from the death of his father, Cumhaill.

"A friend and a dear comrade of yours is here, that is, Fionn the son of Cuadan mac Murchadha, the royal chief of the Fianna of Munster, and the Munster Fianna together with him. We are of one land and one country with you, O Diarmuid, and we will give our bodies and our lives for you and for your sake."

"I will not go out to you," said Diarmuid, "for I will not cause Fionn to be displeased with you for doing well to myself." He drew near to another wattled door and asked who was at it.

"It is Fionn the son of Glor, the royal chief of the Fianna of Ulster, and the Ulster Fianna along with him; and come out to us, and none will dare cut or wound you."

"I will not go out to you," said Diarmuid, "for you are a friend to me, and your father as well; and I would not that you should bear the enmity of Fionn for my sake." He drew near to another wattled door, and asked who was at it.

"No friend to you is any that is here," said they, "for here are Aohd beag of Eamhuin,[2] and Aohd fada of Eamhuin, and Caol crodha of Eamhuin, and Goineach of Eamhuin, and Gothan gilmheurach of Eamhuin, and Aoife the daughter of Gothan gilmheurach of Eamhuin,

∽

[2] *Aohd beag* translates as Aohd the short; *Aohd fada*, Aohd the tall; *Caol crodha*, the slender brave one; *Goineach*, the wounder; *Gothan gilmheurach*, the loud-voiced, white-fingered; *Cuadan lorgaire*, the tracker.

and Cuadan Iorgaire of Eamhuin; and we bear you no love. If you would come out to us we would wound you till you should be like a stone,[1] without respite."

"Evil the company that is there," said Diarmuid, "O you of the lie, and of the tracking, and of the one brogue;[2] and it is not the fear of your hand that is upon me, but from enmity to you that I will not go out to you." He drew near to another wattled door, and asked who was at it.

"Here are Fionn the son of Cumhaill, the son of Art, the son of Treunmhor O'Baoisgne, and four hundred mercenaries with him.[3] We bear you no love, and if you should come out to us we would make opened marrow of your bones."

"I pledge my word," said Diarmuid, "that the door at which you stand, O Fionn, is the very door by which I will pass."

Having heard that, Fionn charged his battalions on pain of their death and their instant destruction not

≈

[1] *Stone* translates the Irish word *gallan*. A gallan is a druidical pillar-stone. Tradition says that fianna members competed at throwing these stones beyond a mark. The phrasing suggests that clanna Eamhuin will either render Diarmuid as dead as a gallan or that they will dispose of him as easily as they would cast a stone aside.

[2] An expression of great contempt.

[3] O'Grady translated the Irish word *amhus* as "hirelings." He explained in a note that the word can also mean a madman, a violent person, or a mercenary soldier.

to let Diarmuid pass them without their knowledge.

Diarmuid having heard that arose with an airy, high, exceeding light bound, by the shafts of his javelins and by the staves of his spears, and landed a great way beyond Fionn and beyond his people without their knowledge or perception. He looked back upon them and proclaimed to them that he had passed them, and slung his shield upon the broad arched expanse of his back, and so went straight westward; and he was not long in going out of sight of Fionn and of the Fianna. Then when he saw that they had not followed him, he turned back where he had seen Aonghus and Grainne depart-ing out of the wood, and he followed them by their track, holding a straight course, until he reached Ros da shoileach.

He found Aonghus and Grainne there in a warm well-lighted hut, and a great wide-flaming fire kin-dled before them, with half a wild boar upon spits. Diarmuid greeted them, and the very life of Grainne all but fled out through her mouth with joy at meeting Diarmuid.

Diarmuid told them his tidings from beginning to end, and they ate their meal that night, and Diarmuid and Grainne went to sleep together until the day came with its full light on the morrow.

Aonghus arose early, and what he said to Diarmuid was, "I will now depart, O son of O'Duibhne, and this counsel I leave you; not to go into a tree having but

67

one trunk when flying before Fionn; and not to go into a cave of the earth to which there is but one door; and not to go onto an island of the sea with but one channel between it and the land. And in whatever place you shall cook your meal, there eat it not; and in whatever place you shall eat, there sleep not; and in whatever place you shall sleep, there rise not on the morrow."[1]

He took leave and farewell of them, and went his way after that. Then Diarmuid and Grainne journeyed with the Siona[2] on their right hand westward until they reached Garbh-abha na bh-Fiann,[3] which is now called Leamhan; and Diarmuid killed a salmon on the bank of the Leamhan, and put it on a spit to broil. Then he himself and Grainne went over across the stream to eat it, as Aonghus had told them; and they went thence westward to sleep.

Diarmuid and Grainne rose early on the morrow, and journeyed straight westward until they reached the marshy moor of Finnliath,[4] and they met a youth upon the moor, and the feature and form of that youth were good, but he had not fitting arms nor

∾

[1] Aonghus advises Diarmuid to change his place of sleep during the night.

[2] *Siona* is the Shannon river.

[3] *Garbh-abha na bh-Fiann* translates as the rough river of the Fianna.

[4] *Finnliath* is the present-day Lea river.

armor. Then Diarmuid greeted that youth, and asked tidings of him.

"I am a young warrior seeking a lord," said he, "and Muadhan is my name."

"What will you do for me, O youth?" said Diarmuid.

"I will do you service by day, and I will watch you by night," said Muadhan.

"I tell you to retain that youth," said Grainne, "for you can not always remain without followers."[5] Then they made bonds of contract and obligation one with the other, and journeyed westward until they reached the Carrthach;[6] and when they had reached the stream, Muadhan asked Diarmuid and Grainne to go upon his back so that he might bear them across over the stream.

"That were a great burden for you," said Grainne. Then he nevertheless took Diarmuid and Grainne upon his back and bore them over across the stream.

They journeyed westward until they reached the Beith,[7] and when they had reached the stream Muadhan did likewise with them, and they went

∾

[5] Grainne suggests that Diarmuid abandon his subservient role within the fianna and, instead, take on the role of cattle lord, one who enters into agreements with clients or followers.

[6] *Carrthach* is the present-day river Carra.

[7] *Beith* is the river Behy in the parish of Glenbehy in county Kerry, the most eastern in the barony of Dunkerron.

into a cave of the earth at the side of Currach cinn adhmuid,[1] over Tonn Toime;[2] and Muadhan dressed a bed of soft rushes and of birch-tops for Diarmuid and Grainne in the further part of that cave.

He himself went into the nearby wood, and plucked in it a straight long rod of a quicken tree; and he put a hair and a hook upon the rod, and put a holly berry upon the hook, and went and stood over the stream, and caught a fish with that cast. He put on a second berry, and caught a second fish; and he put on a third berry, and caught a third fish. He then put the hook and the hair under his girdle, and the rod into the earth, and took his three fish with him to where Diarmuid and Grainne were, and put the fish upon spits. When they were broiled Muadhan said, "I give the dividing of these fish to you, Diarmuid."

"I had rather that you should divide them yourself," said Diarmuid.

"Then," said Muadhan, "I give the dividing of these fish to you, O Grainne."

"It suffices me that you divide them," said Grainne.

"Now had you divided the fish, O Diarmuid," said Muadhan, "you would have given the largest share to

~

[1] *Currach cinn adhmuid* translates as the woody headland of the bog. Brennan identifies it as the mountain Cnoc an dtobar in the Barony of Iveragh overlooking the Dingle Bay.

[2] The *Tonn Toime*, one of the legendary great waves of Ireland, broke on Dingle Bay.

Grainne; and had it been Grainne that divided them, it is to you that she would have given the largest share; and since it is I that am dividing it, have you the largest fish, O Diarmuid, and let Grainne have the second largest fish, and let me have the smallest fish."

(Know, O reader,[3] that Diarmuid kept himself from Grainne, and that he left a spit of flesh uncooked in Doire dha bhoth as a token to Fionn and to the Fianna that he had not sinned with Grainne, and know also that he left the second time seven salmon uncooked upon the bank of the Leamhan, to where Fionn hastened eagerly after him.)

They ate their meal that night, and Diarmuid and Grainne went to sleep in the further part of the cave, and Muadhan kept watch and ward for them until the day arose with its full light on the morrow.

Diarmuid arose early, and made Grainne sit up; and told her to keep watch for Muadhan, and that he himself would go to walk the country. Diarmuid went his way, and went upon the top of the nearest hill to him, and he stood gazing upon the four quarters around him; that is, eastward and westward, southward and northward. He had not been a long time

∾

[3] In Richard J. O'Duffy's 1884 revision of the text, this paragraph and the following are excised. O'Duffy explains in his introduction: "A portion of the translation, which had been unintentionally allowed to remain after the text had been expunged, is now . . . left out" (ix).

there before he saw a great swift fleet, and a fearful company of ships, coming toward the land straight from the west; and the course that the people of the fleet took in coming to land was to the foot of the hill upon which Diarmuid stood. Nine times nine of the chieftains of that fleet came ashore, and Diarmuid went to ask tidings of them; and he greeted them and inquired of them news, of what land or what country they were.

"We are the three royal champions of Muir n-Iocht,"[1] said they, "and Fionn mac Cumhaill has sent for us because of a forest marauder, and a rebellious enemy of his that he has outlawed, who is called Diarmuid O'Duibhne; and to curb him are we now come. Also we have three venomous hounds, and we will loose them upon his track, and it will be but a short time before we get tidings of him; fire burns them not, water drowns them not, and weapons do

∾

[1] *Royal champions of Muir n-Iocht*. O'Grady translates *righfheinnide* as "royal chiefs"; it may also be understood "royal champions," "chief of Fianna," or even simply as "general." *Muir n-Iocht* (the Iccian Sea) is the English channel. It is mentioned by the Four Masters while describing events of A.D. 405: "After Niall of the nine hostages, son of Eochaidh Muighmheadhoin, had been twenty-seven years in the sovereingty of Ireland, he was slain by Eochaidh, son of Enna Ceinnseallach, at Muir n-Iochd, i.e. The sea between France and England." In due course the text will also refer to these warriors as the "people of the green Fianna," so called from the color of their armor or standards.

not wound them; and we ourselves number twenty hundreds of stout stalwart men, and each man of us is a man commanding a hundred. Moreover, tell us who you yourself are, or have you any word of the tidings of the son of O'Duibhne?"

"I saw him yesterday," said Diarmuid, "and I myself am but a warrior who is walking the world by the strength of my hand and the temper of my sword; and I vow that you will have to deal with no ordinary man if Diarmuid meets you."

'Well, no one has been found yet," said they.

"What are you called yourselves?" said Diarmuid.

"Dubh-chosach, Fionn-chosach, and Treun-chosach are our names," said they.[2]

"Is there wine in your ships?" asked Diarmuid.

"There is," said they.

"If you were pleased to bring out a tun[3] of wine," said Diarmuid, "I would perform a feat for you." Certain men were sent to seek the tun, and when it was brought Diarmuid raised it between his two arms and drank a draught out of it, and the others drank the rest of it. After that Diarmuid lifted the tun and

∾

[2] *Dubh-chosach*, *Fionn-chosach*, and *Treun-chosach* translate as the black-footed, the fair-footed, and the strong-footed.

[3] A *tun* is a large cask or barrel. O'Grady comments on the ensuing episode: Either Diarmuid is very cunning or the strangers very stupid. His method of killing them, though efficacious, is scarcely fair.

took it to the top of the hill, and he himself mounted upon it, and rolled it down the steep of the hill until it reached the lower part of it, and he rolled the tun up the hill again, and he did that feat three times in the presence of the strangers, and remained himself upon the tun as it both came and went.

They said that he was one that had never seen a good feat, seeing that he called that a feat; and with that one of them got upon the tun. Diarmuid gave the tun a kick, and the stranger fell to the ground before the tun began to roll; and the tun rolled over that young warrior, so that it caused his bowels and his entrails to come out about his feet. There-upon Diarmuid followed the tun and brought it up again, and a second man mounted upon it. When Diarmuid saw that, he gave it a kick, and the first man had not been more speedily slain than was the second. Diarmuid urged the tun up again, and the third man mounted upon it; and he too was slain like the others. Thus were slain fifty of their people by Diarmuid's trick that day, and as many as were not slain went to their ships that night.

Diarmuid went to his own people, and Muadhan put his hair and his hook upon his rod and caught three salmon. He stuck the rod into the ground, and the hair under his girdle, and took the fish to Diar-muid and Grainne, and they ate their meal that night; and Muadhan dressed a bed under Diarmuid and under Grainne in the further part of the cave, and he went himself to the door of the cave to keep watch and ward for them until the clear bright day arose on the morrow.

Diarmuid arose at early day and beaming dawn on the morrow, and roused Grainne, and told her to watch while Muadhan slept. He went himself to the top of the same hill, and he had not been there long before the three chiefs came toward him, and he enquired of them whether they would like to perform any more feats. They said that they had rather find tidings of the son of O'Duibhne. "I have seen a man who saw him today," said Diarmuid; and thereupon Diarmuid put from him his weapons and his armor upon the hill, every thing but the shirt that was next his skin, and he stuck his javelin, the Crann buidhe of Manannan,[1] upright with its point uppermost. Then Diarmuid rose with a light, bird-like bound, so that he descended from above upon the javelin, and came down fairly and cunningly off it, having neither wound nor cut upon him.

A young warrior of the people of the green Fianna said, "You are one who has never seen a good feat since you would call that a feat"; and with that he put his weapons and his armor from him, and he rose in like manner lightly over the javelin, and descended

～

[1] *Crann buidhe of Manannan* translates as the yellow shaft of Manannan. Irish tales depict Manannan mac Lir as a god of the sea and member of the Tuatha De Danann.

upon it full heavily and helplessly, so that the point of the javelin went up through his heart and he fell down dead to the earth.

Diarmuid drew out the javelin and placed it standing a second time; and the second man of them arose to do the feat, and he too was slain like the other. In this way, fifty of the people of the green Fianna fell by Diarmuid's feat on that day; and they bade him draw out his javelin, saying that he should slay no more of their people with that feat. And they went to their ships.

And Diarmuid went to Muadhan and Grainne, and Muadhan brought them the fish of that night, and Diarmuid and Grainne slept by each other that night, and Muadhan kept watch and ward for them until morning.

Diarmuid rose on the morrow, and took with him to the aforesaid hill two forked poles out of the nearby wood, and placed them upright; and the Moralltach,[1] that is, the sword of Aonghus of the Brugh, between the two forked poles upon its edge. Then he himself rose exceeding lightly over it, and three times measured the sword by paces from the hilt to its point, and he came down and asked if there was a man of them to do that feat.

"That is a bad question," said a man of them, "for

~

[1] *Moralltach* translates as the great and fierce one.

there never was done in Erin any feat which some one of us would not do." He then rose and went over the sword, and as he was descending from above, it happened that one of his legs slipped down on either side of the sword, so that there was made of him two halves to the crown of his head. Then a second man rose, and as he descended from above he chanced to fall crossways upon the sword, so that there were two portions made of him. In these ways, there had not fallen more of the people of the green Fianna of Muir n-Iocht on the two days before that, than there fell upon that day. Then they told him to take up his sword, saying that already too many of their people had fallen by him; and they asked him whether he had gotten any word of the tidings of the son of O'Duibhne.

"I have seen him who saw him today," said Diarmuid, "and I will go to seek tidings tonight."

Diarmuid then went to where Grainne and Muadhan were, and Muadhan caught three fish for them that night; so they ate their meal, and Diarmuid and Grainne went to sleep, and Muadhan kept watch and ward for them.

Diarmuid rose at early dawn of the morning, and girt about him his suit of battle and of conflict, under which, through which, or over which, it was not possible to wound him; and he took the Moralltach, that is, the sword of Aonghus of the Brughh, at his left side, which left no stroke nor blow unfinished at the first trial. He took likewise his two thick-shafted javelins of battle, that is, the Ga buidhe and the Ga dearg,[1] from which none recovered, man or woman, who had ever been wounded by them. After that Diarmuid roused Grainne, and bade her keep watch and ward for Muadhan, saying that he himself would go to view the four heights[2] around him.

When Grainne beheld Diarmuid, brave and daring, clothed in his suit of anger and of battle, fear and great dread seized her, for she knew that it was for a combat and an encounter that he was so equipped; and she asked of him what he intended to do. "You see me thus for fear lest my foes should meet me." That soothed Grainne, and then Diarmuid went in that array to meet the people of the green Fianna of Muir n-Iocht.

They came to land without delay, and enquired of him tidings of the son of O'Duibhne.

"I saw him a while ago," said Diarmuid.

"Then show us where he is," said they, "that we may take his head before Fionn mac Cumhaill."

"I should be keeping him but ill," said Diarmuid, "if I did as you say; for the body and the life of Diarmuid are under the protection of my prowess and of my valor, and therefore I will do him no treachery."

❧

[1] *Ga buidhe* translates as yellow javelin; *Ga dearg*, red javelin.
[2] O'Grady has translated *g-ceithre n-ard* as "four quarters," but more literally it means, "four heights," "four summits," or "four hills."

"Is that true?" said they.

"It is true, indeed," said Diarmuid.

"Then you yourself shall quit this spot," said they, "and we will take your head before Fionn, since you are a foe to him."

"I should doubtless be bound," said Diarmuid, "when I would let my head go with you." And as he thus spoke, he drew the Moralltach from its sheath, and dealt a furious stroke of destruction at the head of him that was next to him, so that he made two fragments of it. Then he drew near to the host of the green Fianna, and set about their destruction and utter confusion heroically and with swift valor, so that he rushed under them, through them, and over them, as a hawk would go through small birds, or a wolf through a large flock of small sheep; even thus it was that Diarmuid hewed cross-ways the glittering very beautiful mail of the men of Lochlann,[3] so that there went not from that spot a man to tell tidings or to boast of great deeds, without having the grievousness of death and the final end of life executed upon him, except the three green champions and a small

~

[3] *Men of Lochlann* is the name given in Irish tales to Vikings or Norsemen. It is not clear that the men of the green Fianna of Muir n-Iocht should be identified as Vikings. Rather, this phrase suggests the quirky, "timeless" quality of the story. Fenian tales, with long formulations in oral and manuscript tradition, often operate without concern for historical propriety.

number of their people that fled to their ship.

Diarmuid returned back having no cut nor wound, and went his way till he reached Muadhan and Grainne. They gave him welcome, and Grainne asked him whether he had gotten any word of the tidings of Fionn mac Cumhaill and of the Fianna of Erin. He said that he had not, and they ate their food and their meat that night.

Diarmuid rose at early day and beaming dawn on the morrow, and halted not until he had reached the aforesaid hill, and having gotten there he struck his shield mightily and soundingly, so that he caused the shore to tremble with the vibration around him.

Then said the chief of the green Fianna, Dubh-chosach, that he would himself go to fight with Diarmuid, and straightways went ashore. Then he and Diarmuid rushed upon one another like wrestlers, bravely, making mighty efforts, ferocious, straining their arms and their swollen sinews, as if they were two savage oxen, or two frenzied bulls, or two raging lions, or two fearless hawks on the edge of a cliff. And this is the form and fashion of the hot, sore, inseparable strife that took place between them.

They both threw their weapons out of their hands, and ran against and to encounter each other, and locked their knotty hands across one another's graceful backs. Then each gave the other a violent mighty twist; but Diarmuid lifted Dubh-chosach upon his shoulder, and hurled his body to the earth, and bound him firm and fast upon the spot. Afterwards came Fionn-chosach and Treun-chosach to combat with him, one after the other; and he bound them with the same binding, and said that he would take their heads from them, were it not that he had rather leave them in those bonds to increase their torments: "for none can loosen you," said he; and he left them there weary and in heavy grief.

As for Diarmuid, he went to look for Muadhan and for Grainne; and they ate their meal and their meat that night, and Diarmuid and Grainne went to sleep, and Muadhan kept watch and ward for them until morning.

Diarmuid rose and told Grainne that their enemies were near them; and he told her the tale of the strangers from beginning to end, how three fifties of their people had fallen three days one after the other by his feats, and how fifteen hundred of their host had fallen on the fourth day by the fury of his hand, and how he had bound the three green chiefs on the fifth day. "And they have three deadly hounds by a chain to do me evil," said he, "and no weapon can wound them."

"Have you taken the heads from those three chiefs?" said Grainne.

"I have not," said Diarmuid, "for I had rather give them long torment than short; for it is not in the power of any warrior nor hero in Erin to loose the binding with which they are bound, but only four;

that is, Oisin the son of Fionn, and Oscar the son of Oisin, and Lughaidh of the Mighty Hand, and Conan mac Morna; and I believe that none of those four will loose them. Nevertheless, Fionn will shortly get tidings of them, and that will sting his heart in his breast; and we must depart out of this cave lest Fionn and the deadly hounds overtake us."

After this, Diarmuid and Grainne and Muadhan came forth out of the cave, and they returned their way back again until they reached the moor of Finn-liath. Grainne began to weary then, and Muadhan took her upon his back until they reached the great Sliabh Luachra.[1] Then Diarmuid sat him down on the brink of the stream which wound through the heart of the mountain; and Grainne was washing her hands, and she asked Diarmuid for his dagger to cut her nails.

As for the strangers, as many of them as were alive, they came upon the hill where the three chiefs were bound and thought to loose them speedily, but those bonds were such that they only drew them tighter upon them.

They had not been long thus before they saw the female messenger of Fionn mac Cumhaill coming with the speed of a swallow, or weasel, or like a blast

⁓

[1] *Sliabh Luachra*, now called in English Slieve Lougher, is the name of the mountainous district east and northeast of Castle-island in county Kerry.

Grainne

of a sharp pure-swift wind, over the top of every high hill and bare mountain toward them; and she inquired of them who it was that had made that great, fearful, destroying slaughter of them.

"Who are you that asks?" said they.

"I am the female messenger of Fionn mac Cumhaill," said she; "and Deirdre of Duibh-shleibhe is my name, and it is to look for you that Fionn has sent me."[1]

"Well then, we know not who he was," said they, "but we will inform you of his appearance; that is, he was a warrior having curling dusky-black hair, and two red ruddy cheeks, and he it is that has made this great slaughter of us; and we are yet more sorely grieved that our three chiefs are bound, and that we cannot loose them; he was likewise three days one after the other fighting with us."[2]

"Which way went that man from you?" said Deirdre.

"He parted from us late last night," said they; "therefore we cannot tell."

"I swear," said Deirdre, "that it was Diarmuid O'Duibhne himself that was there. Bring your hounds with you and loose them on his track, and I will send Fionn and the Fianna of Erin to you."

Then they brought their hounds with them out of their ship, and loosed them upon the track of Diarmuid; but they left a druid attending upon the three chiefs that were bound. The remaining men of

∾

[1] *Deirdre of Duibh-shleibhe* translates as Deirdre of Black Mountain.

[2] Why this is three days instead of five is not clear. *Ag comrac rinn* may be translated "fighting with us" or "at contention with us"; if the latter, the three days may refer to the three days of feats; or the number may simply be a mistake.

the green Fianna followed the hounds upon the track of Diarmuid until they reached the door of the cave, and they went into the back of the cave, and found the bed of Diarmuid and Grainne there. Afterwards they went their way toward the east[3] till they reached the Carrthach, and thence to the moor of Finnliath, and to Garbh-abha na bh-Fiann, which is called Leamhan now, and to the fair plain of Concon, and to the vast and high Sliabh Luachra.

However it may be, Diarmuid did not perceive them coming after him in that pursuit until he beheld the banners of soft silk, and the threatening standards, and three mighty warriors in the fore-front of the hosts, full fierce, and bold, and dauntless, having their three deadly hounds by three chains in their hands. When Diarmuid saw them coming toward him in that manner, he became filled with hatred and great abhorrence of them. And there was a green well-dyed mantle upon him that was in the forefront of the company, and he was out far beyond the others. Then Grainne reached the dagger to Diarmuid, and Diarmuid thrust[4] it upon his thigh,

∾

[3] O'Grady translates *siar* as "west," but it can also mean "back-ward," which in this case means "east," a reading attested to in Shéaghdha's edition of the *Toruigheacht* 40-41.

[4] O'Grady translates *cuir* as "thrust." While a sound translation, the verb *cuirim* has a gradation of meanings, especially when used in conjunction with various nouns and adverbs. It could be translated *put*, *place*, *fix*, *set*, *plant*, *bury*, perhaps even *push in*, *insert* or *stab*.

and said, "I trust you bear the youth of the green mantle no love, Grainne."

"Truly I do not," replied Grainne, "and I would I never to this day had borne love to any." Diarmuid drew his dagger and thrust it into its sheath and went his way after that, and then Muadhan put Grainne upon his back and carried her a mile up the length of the mountain.

It was not long before one of the three deadly hounds was loosed after Diarmuid, and Muadhan told Diarmuid to follow Grainne, saying that he would ward off the hound from him. Then Muadhan went back and took a hound's whelp[1] from beneath his girdle, and set him upon his palm. When the whelp saw the hound rushing toward him, having his jaws and throat open, he rose from Muadhan's palm and sprang into the gullet of the hound, so that he reached the heart and rent it out through his side; and then he sprang back again upon Muadhan's palm, leaving the hound dead after him.

Muadhan followed after Diarmuid and Grainne, and took up Grainne again, and bore her another mile up the mountain. Then was loosed the second hound after them, and Diarmuid spoke to Muadhan,

~

[1] A *whelp* is a puppy. Magical dogs are common in Irish literature. This whelp is reminiscent of the dog that brought forth "a magical wind of druidry" to disarm two sons of the Ri of Ulster (*Tales of the Elders* 156).

Diarmuid and the Hound

and what he said was, "I hear that no spells can be laid upon weapons that wound by magic, nor upon the throat of any beast whatever, and will you stand until I put the Ga dearg through the body, the chest, and the heart of this hound?" and Muadhan and Grainne

87

stood to see that cast.[1] Then Diarmuid aimed a cast at the hound, and put the javelin through his navel, so that he let out his bowels and his entrails, and having drawn out the javelin he followed his own people, that is Grainne and Muadhan.

They had not been long after that before the third hound was loosed upon them; Grainne spoke, and what she said was, "That is the fiercest of them, and I greatly fear him, and keep yourself well against him, O Diarmuid."

It was not long before the hound reached them, and the place where he overtook them was Lic Dhubhain[2] on Sliabh Luachra. He rose with an airy light bound over Diarmuid, and would gladly have seized Grainne, but Diarmuid caught his two hind legs, and struck a blow of his body against the nearest rock, so that he let out his brains through the openings of his head and of his ears.

After that Diarmuid took his arms and his armor, and put his slender-topped finger into the silken string[3] of the Ga dearg, and aimed a triumphant cast at the youth of the green mantle that was in the

∽

[1] Diarmuid is asserting that his magical javelin cannot be countered with magic — "no spells can be laid upon weapons that wound by magic" — and that no magic can protect the throat of any beast. Thus, despite the boasts of the green Fianna, he will try his luck against this hound.

[2] *Lic Dhubhain* translates as the flagstone of Dubhan.

[3] This must have been a string or a loop attached to the shaft of the javelin to assist in hurling it.

forefront of the host, so that he killed him with that cast; he made also a second cast at the second man, and killed him; and the third man he killed likewise. Then, since it is not usual for defense to be made after the fall of lords, when the strangers saw that their chiefs and their lords were fallen, they suffered a complete rout, and took themselves to absolute flight; and Diarmuid pursued them, violently scattering them and slaughtering them, so that unless some one fled over the tops of the forests, or under the green earth, or under the water, there escaped not even a messenger nor a man to tell tidings.

The gloom of death and of instant destruction was executed upon every one of them except Deirdre of Duibh-shleibhe, that is, the female messenger of Fionn mac Cumhaill, who went wheeling and hovering around while Diarmuid was making slaughter of the strangers.

At that very time and hour Fionn saw coming toward him Deirdre of Duibh-shleibhe, with her legs failing, and her tongue raving, and her eyes dropping in her head; and when Fionn saw her come toward him in that plight he asked tidings of her.

"I have great and evil tidings to tell you; and it seems to me that I am one without a lord"; and she told him the tale from first to last of all the slaughter that Diarmuid O'Duibhne had made, and how the three deadly hounds had fallen by him; "and hardly I have escaped myself," said she.

"Where did the son of O'Duibhne go?" said Fionn.

"That I know not," said she. And then Fionn and the Fianna of Erin departed, and no tidings are told of them until they reached Almhuin in Leinster.[1]

As for Fionn, when he heard the tidings of the green Fianna being bound by Diarmuid, he loudly summoned the Fianna of Erin; and they went forth by the shortest ways and by the straightest paths until they reached the hill where the three chiefs were bound, and that was torment of heart to Fionn when he saw them. Then Fionn spoke and what he said was, "O Oisin, loose the three chiefs for me."

"I will not," said Oisin, "for Diarmuid bound me not to loose any warrior whom he should bind."

"O Oscar, loose them," said Fionn.

"No," said Oscar, "I vow that I would delight to put more bonds upon them." Then the son of Lughaidh and Conan also refused to loose them. However, they had not been long at this discourse before the three chiefs died of the hard bonds that were on them. Then Fionn dug three wide-sodded graves for them; and their flag was put over their gravestone, and their names were written in branching ogham,[2]

❧

[1] *Almhuin* is the Hill of Allen, Fionn's stronghold.
[2] Ogham was a method of writing with runes practiced in ancient Ireland. It is formulaically called *Ogham craobh*, or branching ogham, by Irish writers because of the fancied resemblance of its lines to the branches of a tree.

and their burial ceremony was performed, and weary and heavy in heart was Fionn after that.

Touching Diarmuid and Grainne, a further tale is told. They went their way eastward to Sliabh Luachra, and through the territory of the Ui Chonaill Gabhra,[3] and thence with their left hand to the Siona eastward to Ros da shoileach, which is called Luimneach now, and Diarmuid killed for them that night a wild deer; then they ate and drank their fill of flesh and pure water, and slept till the morn on the morrow.

Muadhan rose early and spoke to Diarmuid, and what he said was that he would now depart. "You should not do so," said Diarmuid, "for all that I promised you has been fulfilled without dispute." Muadhan did not suffer Diarmuid to hinder him, and took leave and farewell of them, and left them in that place, and gloomy and grieved were Diarmuid and Grainne after Muadhan.

After that they journeyed on straight northward toward Sliabh Echtghe, and thence to the district of Ui Fhiachrach,[4] and as they passed through that place Grainne wearied; and when she considered that she

∾

[3] *Ui Chonaill Gahbra* may be anglicized Hy Connell Guara. This is the district including the present baronies of Upper and Lower Connello in county Limerick.

[4] *Sliabh Echtghe* is a mountainous district in county Galway on the borders of Clare; the name has been anglicized to Slieve Aughty. *Ui Fhiachrach* was a two-part ruling clan in Connacht: the Ui Fiachrach of Aidne and of Muaidh; the latter is described here.

had no man to carry her but Diarmuid, seeing that Muadhan had departed, courage took possession of her and she set about walking by the side of Diarmuid,[1] until a daring and reckless splash of water leapt up beside her leg, so that she said, "Diarmuid, though your bravery is great in combat and battle, it seems to me that that reckless splash is more intrepid than you."

"That is true, Grainne," said Diarmuid. "Although I have long kept myself from you out of fear of Fionn, I will not suffer myself to be reproached by you any longer; but it is difficult to give trust to a woman."[2] Then and there it was that for the first time Diarmuid O'Duibhne did make a wife of the daughter of the Ri of Ireland, and he bore her with him into the forest.

When they were come into the forest, Diarmuid made a hunting booth in the very midst of the forest, and killed a wild deer that night; so that he and Grainne ate and drank their fill of flesh and pure water. Diarmuid rose early and went to the Searbhan Lochlannach,[3] and made bonds of covenant and com-

~

[1] O'Grady declined to translate the remainder of this paragraph as well as that following. The current editor has translated from the Irish, which was not expunged in O'Grady's text.

[2] *Agus is deacair taobh do thabhairt ris na mnaibh.* I have translated this "but it is difficult to give trust to a woman." It might also be rendered "but it is difficult to take sides with a woman."

[3] *Searbhan Lochlannach* is a giant churl placed as guard over a magical quicken tree by the Tuatha De Danann. Oisin describes the events that led to the quicken tree later in the text.

pact with him, and got from him license to hunt and to chase provided that he would never meddle with his berries.

As for Fionn and the Fianna, having reached Almhuin, they were not long there before they saw fifty warriors coming toward them, and two that were tall, heroic, actively valiant, and who exceeded the others for bulk and beauty in the very front of that company and troop; and Fionn inquired of the Fianna whether they knew them.

"We know them not," they said, "and can you tell who they are, O Fionn?"

"I cannot," said Fionn; "however I think they are enemies to me."

That company of warriors came before Fionn during this discourse, and they greeted him. Fionn answered them and asked tidings of them, and from what land or region they were. They told him that they were indeed enemies to him, that their fathers had been at the slaying of Cumhaill the son of Treunmhor O'Baoisgne at the battle of Cnucha, "and our fathers themselves fell for that act;[4] and it is to ask peace of you we are now come."

"Where were you yourselves when your fathers were slain?" said Fionn.

"In our mothers' wombs," said they, "and our mothers

~

[4] Years after the battle Fionn had killed their fathers as *eric*, or compensation, for the death of his own father.

were two women of the Tuatha De Danann, and we think it time to get our fathers' place and station among the Fianna."

"I will grant you that," said Fionn, "but you must give me eric for my father – I demand his honor price."

"We have no gold, nor silver, nor riches, nor various wealth, kine nor cattle-herds, which we might give you, O Fionn."[1]

"Ask of them no eric, O Fionn," said Oisin, "beyond the fall of their fathers as price for your father."

"It seems to me," said Fionn, "were one to kill me that it would be an easy matter to satisfy you in my eric, O Oisin; and none shall come among the Fianna but he that shall give me eric for my father."

"What eric do you ask?" said Aonghus the son of Art og mac Morna.

"I ask but the head of a warrior, or a fistful of the berries of the quicken tree of Dubhros."

"I will give you good counsel, O children of Morna," said Oisin: "that is to return to where you were reared, and not to ask peace of Fionn as long as you shall live. It is no light matter for you to bring to Fionn anything he is asking of you, for know you what head it is that Fionn asks you to bring him in eric?"

"We do not know," said they.

∽

[1] *Kine* is the archaic plural of cow.

"The head of Diarmuid O'Duibhne is the head that Fionn asks of you, and were you as many in number as twenty hundred men of full strength, Diarmuid O'Duibhne would not let that head go with you, that is, his own head."

"What berries are they that Fionn asks of us?" said they.

"Nothing is more difficult for you to get than those berries," said Oisin, "as I will tell you now. There arose a dispute between two women of the Tuatha De Danann, that is, Aoife the daughter of Manannan, and Aine the other daughter of Manannan the son of Lir. Aoife had become enamored of the son of Lughaidh, that is, the sister's son to Fionn mac Cumhaill, and Aine had become enamored of Lir of Sidhe Fhionnchaid,[2] so that each woman said that her own man was a better hurler than the other; and the fruit of that dispute was that a great hurling match was arranged between the Tuatha De Danann and the Fianna of Erin, and the place where that goal was played was upon a fair plain by Loch Lein of the rough pools.

"The Fianna of Erin and the Tuatha De Danann anwered that call, and these are the noblest and proudest of the Tuatha De Danann that came there; namely, the three Garbhs of Sliabh Mis, and the three

⁓

[2] *Sidhe Fhionnchaidh*, the mound of Fionnchadh, is one of the mounds of the Tuatha De Danann located in the Few Mountains, county Armagh.

Mases of Sliabh Luachra, and the three yellow-haired Murchadhs, and the three Eochaidhs of Aine, and the three heroic Loaghaires, and the three Conalls of Collamhan, and the three Fionns of Fionnmhur, and the three Sgals of Brugh, and the three Ronans of Ath na riogh, and the three Eoghans from Eas ruaidh mhic Bhadhairn, and an Cath-bhuilleach, and the three Fearghuses, and an Glas of Magh Bhreagh, and an Suirgeach suairc from Lionan, and an Mheidhir from Beann liath, and Donn from the Sidhe Breagh, and Fear an bheurla bhinn from the Boyne, and Colla crionchosach from Bearnan Eile, and Donn dumhach, and Donn an oileain, and Donn of Cnoc na n-os, and Donn of Leinchnoc, and Bruithe abhac, and Dolbh the bright-toothed, and the five sons of Fionn Sidhe Chairn Chaoin, and an t-Ilbhreac son of Manannan, and Neamhanach the son of Aonghus, and Bodhbh dearg the son of the Deaghdha, and Manannan the son of Lir, and Abhortach the son of an t-Ioldathach, and Fioghmuin of Fionnmhur, and many others who are not enumerated here.[1]

"We, the Fianna of Erin, and they were for the space of three days and three nights playing the goal from Garbh-abha na bh-Fiann, which is called Leamhan, to Cromghleann of the Fianna,[2] which is called

⌐≈

[1] See the Appendix for translations of most of these names.
[2] *Cromghleann of the Fianna* translates as the crooked valley of the Fenians. This is the valley of the river Flesk. Rising near the

Glen Fleisge now; and neither of us won a goal.

"Now the whole of the Tuatha De Danann were all that time without our knowledge on either side of Loch Lein, and they understood that if we, the Fianna, were united, all the men of Erin could not win the goal from us. And the counsel which the Tuatha De Danann took was to depart back again and not to play out that match with us. The provisions that the Tuatha De Danann had brought with them from Tir Tairngire[3] were these: crimson nuts, and catkin apples, and fragrant berries; and as they passed through the district of Ui Fhiachrach by the Muaidh,[4] one of the berries fell from them, and a quicken tree grew from that berry, and that quicken tree and its berries have many virtues; for no disease or sickness seizes any one that eats three berries of them, and they who eat feel the exhilaration of wine and the satisfying of old mead; and were it at the age of a century, he that tasted them would return again to be thirty years old.

"When the Tuatha De Danann heard that those virtues belonged to the quicken tree, they placed a guard over it, that is, the Searbhan Lochlannach, a

~

eastern borders of Kerry, the river flows with a winding course westward, through what was a very wild and mountainous country, into Loch Lein (the Lake of Killarney).

[3] *Tir Tairngire* is the Land of Promise.

[4] *Muaidh* is the present-day river Moy in county Sligo.

youth of their own people, that is, a thick-boned, large-nosed, crooked-tusked, red-eyed, swart-bodied giant of the children of wicked Cam the son of Naoi;[1] whom neither weapon wounds, nor fire burns, nor water drowns, so great is his magic. He has but one eye only in the fair middle of his black forehead, and there is a thick collar of iron round that giant's body, and he is fated not to die until there be struck upon him three strokes of the iron club that he has. He sleeps in the top of that quicken tree by night, and he remains at its foot by day to watch it; and those, O children of Morna, are the berries which Fionn asks of you," said Oisin.

"Nevertheless, it is not easy for you to meddle with them by any means; for that Searbhan Lochlannach has made a wilderness of the districts around him, so that Fionn and the Fianna dare not chase or hunt there for the dread of that terrible one."

Aodh the son of Andala mac Morna spoke, and what he said was that he had rather perish in seeking those berries than go back again to his mother's country; and he asked Oisin to keep his people until they returned again; and should he and his brother fall in that adventure, to restore his people to Tir Tairngire. And those two good warriors took leave

～

[1] *Cam the son of Naoi* is Ham or Cham, the son of Noah. He is generally distinguished in Irish writings by the epithet *collach*, wicked, or more strictly, incestuous.

and farewell of Oisin and of the chiefs of the Fianna, and went their way; nor is it told how they fared until they reached Ros da shoileach, which is called Luimneach now, and it is not told how they were entertained that night.

They rose early on the morrow, and did not stop until they reached Dubhros of Ui Fhiachrach, and as they went toward the forest they found the track of Diarmuid and Grainne there, and they followed the track to the door of the hunting booth in which were Diarmuid and Grainne.

Diarmuid heard them coming to the hunting booth, and stretched an active warrior hand over his broad weapons, and asked who they were that were at the door.

"We are of the Clan Morna," said they.

"Which of the Clan Morna are you?" said Diarmuid.

"Aodh the son of Andala mac Morna, and Aonghus the son of Art og mac Morna," said they.

"Why are you come to this forest?" said Diarmuid.

"Fionn mac Cumhaill has sent us to seek your head, if you be Diarmuid O'Duibhne."

"I am he, indeed," said Diarmuid.

"Well then," said they, "Fionn will not choose but get your head, or the full of his fist of the berries of the quicken of Dubhros from us in eric for his father."

"It is no easy matter for you to get either of those things," said Diarmuid, "and woe to him that may fall under the power of that man. I also know that it was he who slew your fathers, and surely that should suffice him as payment from you."

"Truly it should suffice you," said Aodh the son of Andala mac Morna, "to have taken his wife from Fionn, without reviling him."

"It is not to revile him I say that," said Diarmuid, "but once before I saw him do the like to Conan the son of Fionn of Liathluachra, as I will relate to you now."

On a day when Fionn was in Teamhair Luachra,[1] with the chiefs and great nobles of the Fenians of Erin by him,[2] they were not long before they saw a tall, warriorlike, actively valiant youth coming toward them, completely arrayed in weapons and armor; and Fionn asked the Fianna of Erin whether they knew him. They all everyone said that they knew him not.

"But I do," said Fionn, "I perceive that he is an enemy to me."

❧

[1] *Teamhair Luachra* was also called Teamhair Earann, being the royal residence of the country of the Earna, or descendants of Oilioll Earann, commonly called in English the Ernans of Munster. It was situated in the district of Sliabh Luachra. The site of the fort is marked by Beul atha na Teamhrach, a ford on a small stream, near Castleisland in county Kerry.

[2] I have not used quotation marks to delimit the story of Cian's worm as told by Diarmuid. The extended use of double and single marks becomes especially confusing when Oisin takes over the storytelling and is unnecessary for a clear understanding of the text.

The youth came before them after that, and greeted them. Fionn asked tidings of him, who he was, or from what country or what region he came.

"Conan the son of Fionn of Liathluachra is my name," said he, "and my father was at the slaying of your father at the battle of Cnucha, and he perished himself for that act, and it is to ask for his place among the Fianna that we are now come."[3]

"You will obtain that," said Fionn, "but you must give me eric for my father."

"Ask no further eric of him," said Oisin, "since his father fell by you."

"I will not take that from him," said Fionn. "I must have more eric from him."

"What eric do you ask?" said Conan.

"It is but the large-headed worm of Cian the son of Oilioll Oluim. Bring its head to me in eric of my father," said Fionn.

"I give you a good counsel, O Conan," said Oisin, "to return to where you were born, and to ask no peace of Fionn so long as he shall live."

"What is that worm," asked Conan, "that I should not cut off its head?"

"It is this," said Oisin, and he spoke the following words. One time Oilioll Oluim went forth out of Dun[4] Eocharmhuighe, with Sadhbh the daughter of Conn

~

[3] The Irish frequently use the first person plural for emphasis.
[4] A *dun* is a fort or stronghold.

of the hundred battles, his wife and his mate, along with him, both in the same chariot. Sadhbh was then heavy and pregnant, and she saw a blackthorn branch over her head covered with sloes. A desire for those sloes came upon her, and Oilioll shook the branch over the upper board of the chariot, so that Sadhbh ate her fill of them. They returned home again, and Sadhbh bore a smooth fair lusty son of that heavy pregnancy, that is, Cian the son of Oilioll Oluim; and the Ri of Ciarruidhe Luachra[1] took him with him to rear him. Now that boy was born with a caul across his head,[2] and as the boy grew and increased so also the caul increased.

Cian grew until he had completed twenty years, and Oilioll had two other sons, and those three were then of full strength. They had three servants, and at a certain time the servants went to the house of Sgathan the son of Scannlan to be entertained. Sgathan used them well that night, and said, "There is a feast tonight in this house prepared for Fionn mac Cumhaill, but you will be well and plentifully fed elsewhere, even though you do not come to that feast."

༄

[1] *Ciarruidhe Luachra* is the ancient name for the territory that is now comprised by county Kerry, and which takes its name from Ciar, one of its ancient monarchs.

[2] A caul is a translucent membrane, a portion of the amniotic sac, which sometimes fastens over a portion of a baby's body at birth. Folk belief has usually thought it a good omen when a child is born with a caul over its head.

They ate their food that night, and arose early on the morrow, and returned back to Dun Eocharmhuighe, and the three sons of Oilioll Oluim were before them on the plain; that is, Eoghan mor, Cormac Cas, and Cian. Eoghan inquired of his servant where he had been the last night. "We were in the house of Sgathan the son of Scannlan."

"How did you fare there?" asked Eoghan. "We fared well," said the servant. Cormac asked. "Well," said the servant. Cian asked his servant the same thing. "We fared ill," said Cian's servant, "for he boasted to us that he had prepared a feast for Fionn mac Cumhaill, and he did not suffer us to taste it."

"Believe him not," said the other servants, "for we were all used well."

"He shall pay me for not using my servant well," said Cian.

"Say not that," said Cormac Cas, "for he is my fencing partner, and he has a sufficient lord,[3] that is Fionn mac Cumhaill."

"I care not," said Cian, "I will go to him to be shaved."

Now Cian was so that no man ever shaved him but he would take his head from him, and Cian went his way until he came to the Dun of Sgathan, the son of Scannlan. Sgathan chanced to be on the plain before

~

[3] That is to say Fionn, his chief, would be able to avenge an injury done to his dependant.

him, and Cian asked him to shave him. "I will do so," said Scannlan,[1] "for that is my trade, to shave; and over there is the house where I do it; go on before me to it"; and Cian went to the house.

Sgathan went to his sleeping house, and put on his arms and his armor, and then he brought a knife and water in his hand, and went to where Cian was.

"Why have you brought those weapons with you?" said Cian.

"I hear," said Scannlan, "that you slay everyone who shaves you, but nevertheless I will shave you for the future."

After that Sgathan loosed the binding which was upon the head of Cian, and found a large caul from ear to ear upon him. "Is this the reason that you kill everyone who shaves you?" asked Sgathan. "It surely is," said Cian, "but you need not fear me."

"I pledge my word," said Sgathan, "that I will now do what would cause you to slay me, so that I may know what reason you have here."[2]

Upon that he gave a rip of the knife across the caul, so that a worm sprang out of it, and rose with a swift very light bound until it reached the very

∾

[1] That is Sgathan, the son of Scannlan.
[2] Despite Cian's reassurance, Sgathan is purposeful when stating that he will commit the act, i.e. cut the caul. Pledging his word is typically Irish and shows his determination to complete the dangerous act, for no honorable Irishman would break his word.

top of the dwelling; and as it descended from above it met the spear of Cian, and twisted itself in hard firm indissoluble knots about the head of the spear. After Cian's head was shaved Sgathan would gladly have killed the worm, but Cian said not to kill it until he himself should take it to Sadhbh, the daughter of Conn of the hundred battles, "for in her womb that worm was generated."

After that, Sgathan applied balsams and healing herbs to the wounds of Cian, and Cian went his way to Dun Eocharmhuighe bearing his spear before him, and the worm knotted to it.

Oilioll Oluim and Sadhbh chanced to be before him upon the plain, and Cian told them the story of the worm from first to last. Oilioll said to kill the worm, but Sadhbh said that it should not be killed, "for we know not," said she, "but that it and Cian may be fated to have the same span of life." And the counsel upon which Oilioll and Sadhbh determined was this, to put a strong palisade of wood around it, and to send it every day nourishment and a plentiful portion of meat and drink.

That worm grew and increased so that it was necessary to open the enclosure round it, and to build for it a very sturdy and larger house. In this way it grew and increased to the end of a year, so that there were a hundred heads upon it, and it mattered not into which head came the food that was sent to it, and it would swallow a hero or a warrior with his arms and his armor in each of its greedy ravening heads.

Now at that very time and season the Ri of Ciar-ruidhe Luachra came to see his foster-son, Cian the son of Oilioll; and when he had heard the account of that worm he went to gaze and marvel at it, and rose and stood upon the top of the wall.

When the worm got sight of him it gave an eager, deadly, hostile spring upon him, so that it lopped off his leg from the thigh down; and when the women and the children of the place saw that deed, they all fled and left the Dun deserted and empty after them. When Oilioll heard that, he said that the worm should be slain lest it might do some greater horror than even that, and Sadhbh consented that it should be slain.

When the household had gotten that leave, they kindled the Dun into a dusky-red crimson-flaming blaze of fire around the worm. Then when the worm felt the heat of the fire touching it and the house falling upon it, it rose upwards with an airy exceeding light spring through the roof of the house, and went its ways westward with the household after it, until it reached the dark cave of Fearna in the district of Corca Ui Dhuibhne.[1] It entered into the cave and made a wilderness of the district round about it, so that Fionn and the Fenians of Erin dare not either

~

[1] The *Corca Ui Dhuibhne* controlled the area of the Dingle Peninsula, now the barony of Corcaguiney, in county Kerry.

chase or hunt there during the life of that worm. And its head it is that Fionn asks of thee, O Conan, said Oisin.

"Nevertheless," said Conan, "I had rather meet my death in seeking that eric than go back again where I was reared."

At that he took leave and farewell of Oisin and of the chiefs of the Fianna, and went his way to the place where the worm was. When Conan beheld it he put his finger into the silken loop of the Ga dearg. "It was I myself that had lent him the Ga dearg," said Diarmuid, "for I had conceived an attachment and affection for him; for I knew that nothing in the world could slay it unless the Ga dearg did." And he made a careful cast of it, so that he put it through the navel of the worm, and killed it by virtue of that cast, and took one of its heads into the presence of Fionn; and when Fionn knew the head, he said that he would not be content without getting further eric from Conan for his father.

Now at that very time and season there came toward the hill where we all were then, a mighty very swift stag; and we all followed the stag. When Conan saw that, he covered the retreat of the Fianna, and he himself and Fionn followed the stag; and no tidings are told of them until they reached us at evening time, and a hind quarter of the stag upon Conan's shoulder as he followed Fionn, and Fionn never required eric from Conan from that time to this.

"And by your hands, O children of Morna," said Diarmuid, "we know not whether it was fairly or by force that Conan made Fionn grant him peace that day. And I think that was not more unjust than to require of you too eric for his father, seeing it should suffice him that you were yet in your mothers' wombs when your fathers fell by him, without sending you to seek the quicken berries of Dubhros or my head, for that is the warrior's head that Fionn requires of you; and which ever of these things you shall take him, you will not get peace after all."

"What berries are those that Fionn requires," asked Grainne, "that they cannot be got for him?"

"They are these," said Diarmuid: "the Tuatha De Danann left a quicken tree in the district of Ui Fhiach-rach, and in all berries that grow upon that tree there are many virtues, that is, there is in every berry of them the exhilaration of wine and the satisfying of old mead; and whoever should eat three berries of that tree, had he completed a hundred years he would return to the age of thirty years. Nevertheless there is a giant, hideous and foul to behold, keeping that quicken tree; every day he is at the foot of it, and every night he sleeps at the top. Moreover, he has made a desert of the district round about him, and he can not be killed until three terrible strokes are struck upon him with an iron club that he has, and that club is thus; it has a thick ring of iron through its end, and the ring around the giant's body; he has moreover forced a covenant with Fionn and with the Fianna of Erin not to hunt in that district, and when Fionn outlawed me and became my enemy, I got of him leave to hunt, provided that I should never meddle with the berries. And, O children of Morna," said Diarmuid, "choose you between combat with me for my head, and going to seek the berries from the giant."

"I swear by the rank of my tribe among the Fianna," said each of the children of Morna, "that I will do battle with you first."

Thereupon those good warriors, that is, the children of Morna and Diarmuid, harnessed their handsome bodies in their array of weapons of valor and battle, and the combat that they resolved upon was to fight by the strength of their hands.[1]

The outcome of the contest was that Diarmuid overcame them and bound them both upon that spot. "You have fought that strife well," said Grainne, "and I vow that even if the children of Morna go not to seek those berries, I will never lie in your bed unless I get a portion of them, although that is no fit thing for a woman to do being pregnant; and I indeed am now heavy and pregnant, and I shall not live if I taste not those berries."

"Force me not to break peace with the Searbhan

---

[1] *By the strength of their hands* alone, i.e. without weapons.

Lochlannach," said Diarmuid, "for he would not the more readily let me take them."

"Loose these bonds from us," said the children of Morna, "and we will go with you, and we will give ourselves for your sake."

"You shall not come with me," said Diarmuid, "for were you to see one glimpse of the giant, you would more likely die than live after it."

"Then do us the grace," said they, "to slacken the bonds on us, and to let us go with you privately that we may see your battle with the giant before you hew the heads from our bodies"; and Diarmuid did so.

Then Diarmuid went his way to the Searbhan Lochlannach, and the giant chanced to be asleep before him. He dealt him a stroke of his foot, so that the giant raised his head and gazed up at Diarmuid, and what he said was, "Do you wish to break peace, O son of O'Duibhne?

"It is not that," said Diarmuid, "but that Grainne the daughter of Cormac is heavy and pregnant, and she has conceived a desire for those berries which you have, and it is to ask the full of a fist of those berries from you that I am now come."

"I swear," said the giant, "were it even that you should have no children except that birth now in her womb, and were there but Grainne of the race of Cormac the son of Art, and were I sure that she should perish in bearing that child, that she should never taste one berry of those berries."

Searbhan Lochlannach

"I may not do you treachery," said Diarmuid; "therefore I now tell you that I come to seek them by fair means or foul."

The giant, having heard that, rose up and stood, and put his club over his shoulder, and dealt Diarmuid

111

three mighty strokes, so that he wrought him some little hurt in spite of the shelter of his shield. And when Diarmuid marked the giant off his guard he cast his weapons upon the ground, and made an eager exceeding strong spring upon the giant, so that he was able with his two hands to grasp the club. Then he lifted the giant from the earth and hurled him round him, and the iron ring that was about the giant's body and through the end of the club stretched, and when the club reached Diarmuid he struck three mighty strokes upon the giant, so that he dashed his brains out through the openings of his head and of his ears, and left him dead without life; and those two of the Clan Morna were looking at Diarmuid as he fought that strife.

When they saw the giant fall they too came forth, and Diarmuid sat him down weary and spent after that combat, and asked the children of Morna to bury the giant under the brushwood of the forest, so that Grainne might not see him, "and after that go you to seek her also, and bring her." The children of Morna drew the giant forth into the wood, and buried him, and went after Grainne and brought her to Diarmuid. "There, O Grainne," said Diarmuid, "are the berries you asked for. Pluck of them whatever pleases you."

"I swear," said Grainne, "that I will not taste a single berry of them but the berry that your hand shall pluck, O Diarmuid." Thereupon Diarmuid rose and stood, and plucked the berries for Grainne and for the children of Morna, so that they ate their fill of them.

When they were filled Diarmuid spoke, and said, "O children of Morna, take as many as you can of these berries, and tell Fionn that it was you yourselves that slew the Searbhan Lochlannach."

"We swear," said they, "that we grudge what we shall take to Fionn of them"; and Diarmuid plucked them a load of the berries. Then the children of Morna spoke their gratitude and thanks to Diarmuid after the favors they had received from him, and went their way to Fionn and the Fianna of Erin.

Now Diarmuid and Grainne went into the top of the quicken tree, and laid them in the bed of the Searbhan Lochlannach, and the berries below were but bitter berries compared to the berries that were above upon the tree.

The children of Morna reached Fionn, and Fionn asked their news of them from first to last. "We have slain the Searbhan Lochlannach," said they, "and have brought the berries of Dubhros in eric for your father, if by chance we may get peace for them."

Then they gave the berries into the hand of Fionn, and he knew the berries, and put them under his nose, and said to the children of Morna, "I swear," said Fionn, "that it was Diarmuid O'Duibhne that gathered these berries, for I know the smell of O'Duibhne's skin on them, and full sure I am that he it was that slew the Searbhan Lochlannach; and I will go to learn whether he is alive at the quicken

The Quicken Tree

tree. But it shall profit you nothing to have brought the berries to me, and you shall not get your fathers' place among the Fianna until you give me payment for my father."

After that he caused the seven battalions of the

standing Fianna to assemble in one place, and he went his way to Dubhros of Ui Fiachrach; and followed Diarmuid's track to the foot of the quicken tree, and found the berries without any watch upon them, so that they all ate their fill of them. The great heat of the noon day then overtook them, and Fionn said that he would stay at the foot of the quicken tree till that heat should be past: "for I know that Diarmuid is in the top of the tree."

"It is a great sign of envy in you,[1] O Fionn, to suppose that Diarmuid would abide in the top of the quicken tree, and he knowing that you are intent on slaying him," said Oisin.

After this Fionn asked for a fidchell[2] board to play, and he said to Oisin, "I would play a game with you upon this board." They sat down at either side of the board; namely, Oisin and Oscar and the son of Lughaidh and Diorruing the son of Dobhar O'Baoisgne on one side, and Fionn upon the other side.

Thus they were playing that game of fidchell with skill and exceeding cunning, and Fionn so played the

❧

[1] The meaning seems to be that envy and anger have caused Fionn to judge foolishly in supposing Diarmuid in such a place.
[2] O'Grady translates the Irish *fithcheall* as chess, which suggests a better understanding of this ancient game than we possess. Repeatedly mentioned in Irish literature, it is a board game in which two players move game pieces, or fidchell men (*fear fithchille*) across a game board.

game that Oisin had but one move alone to make, and what Fionn said was, "One move there is to win you the game, O Oisin, and I dare all that are by you to show you that move."

Then said Diarmuid in the hearing of Grainne, "I grieve that you are thus in a strait about a move, O Oisin, and that I am not there to teach you that move."

"It is worse for you," said Grainne, "that you are yourself in the bed of the Searbhan Lochlannach, in the top of the quicken tree, with the seven battalions of the standing Fianna round about you intent upon your destruction, than that Oisin should lack that move."

Then Diarmuid plucked one of the berries, and aimed at the man that should be moved; and Oisin moved that man and thus turned the game against Fionn. They began to play again and Oisin was again worsted. When Diarmuid beheld that, he struck a second berry upon the man that should be moved; and Oisin moved that man and turned the game against Fionn in like manner. When Fionn was carrying the game against Oisin the third time, Diarmuid struck a third berry upon the man that would give Oisin the game, and the Fianna raised a mighty shout at that game. Fionn spoke, and what he said was, "I marvel not at your winning that game, O Oisin, seeing that Oscar is doing his best for you, and that you have with you the zeal of Diorruing, the skilled knowledge of the son of Lughaidh, and the prompting of the son of O'Duibhne."

"It shows great envy in you, O Fionn," said Oscar, "to think that Diarmuid O'Duibhne would stay in the top of this tree with you in wait for him."

"With which of us is the truth, O son of O'Duibhne," said Fionn, "with me or with Oscar?"

"You did never err in your good judgment, O Fionn," said Diarmuid. "I, indeed, and Grainne are here in the bed of the Searbhan Lochlannach." Then Diarmuid caught Grainne, and gave her three kisses in the presence of Fionn and the Fianna.

"It grieves me more that the seven battalions of the standing Fianna and all the men of Erin should have witnessed you the night you took Grainne from Teamhair, seeing that you were my guard that night, than that these that are here should witness you; and you shall give your head for those kisses," said Fionn.

Thereupon Fionn arose with the four hundred mercenaries that he had on wages and on stipend, with intent to kill Diarmuid; and Fionn put their hands into each others' hands round about that quicken tree, and warned them on pain of losing their heads, and as they would preserve their life, not to let Diarmuid pass out by them. Moreover, he promised them that to whatever man of the Fianna of Erin should go up and bring him the head of Diarmuid, he would give his arms and his armor, with his father's and his grandfather's rank among the Fianna freely.

Garbh of Sliabh Cua[1] answered, and what he said was that it was Diarmuid's father, Donn O'Donnchudha, who had slain his father, and to requite that he would go to avenge him upon Diarmuid, and he went his way up.

Now it was shown to Aonghus of the Brugh, Diarmuid's foster-father, what a strait Diarmuid was in, and he came to aid him without knowledge or perception of the Fianna; and when Garbh of Sliabh Cua had got up into the top of the quicken tree, Diarmuid gave him a stroke of his foot and flung him down into the midst of the Fianna, so that Fionn's mercenaries took off his head, for Aonghus had put the form of Diarmuid upon him. After he was slain his own shape came upon him again, and Fionn and the Fianna of Erin knew him, so that they said that it was Garbh that was fallen.

Then said Garbh of Sliabh Crot[2] that he would go to avenge his father also upon the son of O'Duibhne, and he went up, and Aonghus gave him a stroke of his foot, so that he flung him down in the midst of

[1] *Sliabh Cua* is the name applied in ancient times to the mountain now known as Cnoc Maoldomhnaigh, anglicized Knockmeledown, on the borders of the counties Tipperary and Waterford.

[2] *Sliabh Crot*, anglicized as Mount Grud, is in the barony of Clanwilliam, county Tipperary. The battle of Sliabh Crot was fought here in the year 1058 between Diarmuid Mac Maelnambo and Donchadh, the son of Brian Boruma.

the Fianna with the form of Diarmuid upon him, and Fionn's people took off his head; and Fionn said that that was not Diarmuid but Garbh, for Garbh took his own form again.

Garbh of Sliabh Guaire[3] said that he too would go, and that it was Donn O'Donnchudha that had slain his father, and that therefore he would go to avenge him upon the son of O'Duibhne, and he climbed into the top of the quicken tree. Diarmuid gave him also a stroke of his foot, so that he flung him down, and Aonghus put the form of Diarmuid upon him, so that the Fianna killed him. Now the nine Garbhs of the Fianna were thus slain under a false appearance by the people of Fionn.

As for Fionn, after the fall of the nine Garbhs of the Fianna, namely, Garbh of Sliabh Cua, and Garbh of Sliabh Crot, and Garbh of Sliabh Guaire, and Garbh of Sliabh Muice, and Garbh of Sliabh Mor, and Garbh of Sliabh Lugha, and Garbh of Ath Fraoich, and Garbh of Sliabh Mis, and Garbh of Drom Mor, he was full of anguish and of faintheartedness and of grief.

Aonghus then said that he would take Grainne with him. "Take her," said Diarmuid, "and if I be alive at evening I will follow you; and if Fionn kills me, whatever children Grainne may have rear and bring

[3] *Sliabh Guaire*, anglicized Slieve Gorey, is a mountainous district in the barony of Clankee in county Cavan.

them up well, and send Grainne to her own father at Teamhair."

Aonghus took leave and farewell of Diarmuid, and flung his magic mantle round about Grainne and about himself, and they departed, trusting in the mantle, without knowledge of the Fianna, and no tidings are told of them until they reached the Brugh na Boyne.

Then Diarmuid O'Duibhne spoke, and what he said was, "I will go down to you, O Fionn, and to the Fianna; and I will deal slaughter and utter confusion upon you and upon your people, seeing that I am certain your wish is to allow me no deliverance, but to work my death in some place; and moreover, seeing that it is not mine to escape from this danger which is before me, since I have no friend nor companion in the far regions of the great world under whose safe-guard or protection I may go, because full often have I wrought death and desolation upon the warriors of the world for love of you. For there never came upon you battle nor combat, strait nor extremity in my time, but I would adventure myself into it for your sake and for the sake of the Fianna, and moreover I used to do battle before you and after you.[1] And I swear, O Fionn, that I will well avenge myself, and that you shall not get me for nothing."

~

[1] Diarmuid suggests that he cleared the way for Fionn going into battle and covered his retreat when leaving it.

"Therein Diarmuid speaks truth," said Oscar, "and give him mercy and forgiveness."

"I will not," said Fionn, "to all eternity; and he shall not get peace nor rest forever till he give me satisfaction for every slight that he has put upon me."

"It is a foul shame and sign of jealousy in you to say that," said Oscar; "and I pledge the word of a true warrior," said he, "that unless the firmament fall down upon me, or the earth open beneath my feet,[2] I will not suffer you nor the Fianna of Erin to give him cut nor wound; and I take his body and his life under the protection of my bravery and my valor, vowing that I will take him away safely in spite of the men of Erin. And, O Diarmuid, come down out of the tree, since Fionn will not grant you mercy. I take you, pledging my body and my life that no evil shall be done to you today."

Then Diarmuid rose and stood upon a high branch of the tree, and rose up with an airy bound, light, bird-like, by the shafts of his spears, so that he landed on the two soles of his feet on the grass-green earth,

∾

[2] Oscar is invoking a well-known Celtic oath that promises duty as long as the sea does not drown, the sky fall upon, or the earth swallow up the promise giver; that is, the promise will be kept as long as the earth remains as we know it. The longevity of this oath is attested by Strabo's misrecorded version in 335 B.C. when Celtic emissaries first met Alexander the Great. See Cunliffe, *The Ancient Celts* 80.

and he passed out far beyond Fionn and the Fianna of Erin.

And here in this lay is fully set down every dispute and every word that came to pass between the Fianna from their first coming to the tree until they and Diarmuid parted from one another.[1]

> I remember the play
> Which the chief of the Fianna played,
> Which Fionn played and his son,
> At Bun Irse in the west.

> I myself sat down to the table,
> I myself and my two sons,
> At the shoulder of Fionn O'Baoisgne,
> Alas! to us it was pleasant.

> The fidchell board was put betwixt us,
> Both chief and warrior;

[1] Most old Irish stories, and even many historical works, contain poetical accounts of speeches, episodes, etc., which are generally not the composition of the writer, but quotations, and consequently often in much older language than the prose in which they are inserted. This is an Ossianic poem purporting to be an account of this fidchell game given to St. Patrick in later times (most likely) by Oisin. The poem interleaves references to the contest on the game board with references to the approaching encounter between Fionn and his followers and Diarmuid and Oscar.

The men were playing,
And that was no trifling play.

Diarmuid, the white-toothed, throws
A berry from above upon the table;
Oisin raises it speedily,
And puts a man in its place.

Fionn said at last,
"There is someone in the tree;
And that will be a terrific slaughter
Which we shall have against him."

Then spoke Oscar,
The son of the fierce noble Oisin;
"O Ri, which of the men
Is he for whom thou wishest?"

Then Fionn: "Set me not astray,
O man, though good thy hand,
For that is the dreadful slaughter
Which we shall have about the table."

Then Oscar. "Say not that, O Ri,
And let there not be constant displeasure in thy face;
Were Diarmuid hateful to thee
It were fitting to leave him to us."

Then spoke Faolan,
And he inciting the heroes;
"We will not let Diarmuid go
With anyone that lives."

"Foul fall thee, Oscar,
O man that incitest every battle,
That sayest thou wouldst take with thee a warrior,
In spite of me and my father."

Then Oscar: "Come down, O Diarmuid,
I myself take thee in hand,
Vowing that I will bear thee safe
By force from the Fianna of Erin."

"Thy words are big, O Oscar,"
Said gloomy Goll of the strokes,
"To say that thou wouldst bear away a warrior
By force from the assembly of the men of Erin."

Then Oscar: "'Tis not thou that incitest
    against me, O Goll,
The swift clans of the great deeds,
The clans hostile to Diarmuid,
The clans that challenge a mighty warrior."

Then Goll: "If that be thy speech,
O warrior of the hard fights,

Let thy blows be proved to us,
In that combat which thou undertakest."

Then speaks Coirriol
With a loud voice to Oscar;
"That combat which thou hast undertaken,
Thou wilt have to go and maintain it."

Then spoke Oscar,
And that was the fierce answer;
"I will hew your bones,
Both son and father."

The son of O'Duibhne leaps
Down from the top of the tree,
His body bound in his battle harness,
That was the wondrous noise.

Five hundred, O Patrick,
Though many it seems, of our chiefs,
Opposed the son of O'Duibhne,
Ere he reached Oscar.

Oscar drew and cast his spear,
Like the sound of the wind and glen,
Or like the sound of water rushing over a flagstone,
Whilst he dispersed the warriors.

Then speaks Conan,
Continually abiding in enmity;
"Suffer the Clanna Baoisgne
To hew each other's flesh."

Fionn spoke lastly,
"Restrain your weapons;
Let not the Clanna Morna be after you,
Until ye go to Almhuin."

Then departed from us together
Diarmuid O'Duibhne, the white-toothed,
And Oscar of the great deeds,
Who left us in the pains of death.

After that combat Oscar and Diarmuid proceeded onwards, neither one or other of them being cut nor wounded, and no tidings are told of them until they reached the Brugh na Boyne, and Grainne and Aonghus met them with joy and good courage. Then Diarmuid told them his tidings from first to last, and Grainne nearly fell into a numb stupor of instant dissolution and death through the fear and the horror of that story.

Touching Fionn, after the departure of the son of O'Duibhne and of Oscar, he found nine chieftains and ten hundred warriors in a mangled bloody mass, and he sent every one that was curable where he might be healed, and dug a broad-sodded grave, and put into it every one that was dead. Heavy, weary, and mournful was Fionn after that time, and he swore and vowed that he would take no rest until he should have avenged upon Diarmuid all that he had done to him.

Then he told his trusty people to equip his ship, and to put a store of meat and drink into her. Thus did they and, the ship being ready, he himself and a thousand warriors of his people together with him went their way to the ship. They immediately weighed her anchors, and urged the ship forward with a mighty exceeding strong rowing, so that they launched her forth the space of nine waves into the blue-streamed ocean, and they caught the wind in the bosom of the sails of the mast, and it is not told how they fared until they took haven and harbor in the north of Alba.[1]

They made fast the ship to the mooring posts of the harbor, and Fionn with five of his people went to the dun of the Ri of Alba, and Fionn struck the knocker upon the door, so that the doorkeeper asked who was there; and it was told him that Fionn mac Cumhaill was there.

"Let him be admitted," said the Ri. Fionn was thereupon admitted, and he himself and his people went before the Ri. A kindly welcome was made for

∼

[1] *Alba* is northern Scotland.

Fionn by the Ri, and he caused Fionn to sit down in his own place.[1] Thereafter were given to them mead mild and pleasant to drink, and strong fermented drinks, and the Ri sent to fetch the rest of the people of Fionn, and he made them welcome in the dun. Then Fionn told the Ri the cause and matter for which he was come from beginning to end, and that it was to seek counsel and aid against the son of O'Duibhne that he was then come. "And truly you ought to give me a host,[2] for Diarmuid O'Duibhne it was that slew your father and your two brothers and many of your chiefs likewise."

"That is true," said the Ri, "and I will give you my own two sons and a host of a thousand about each man of them." Joyful was Fionn at the company that the Ri of Alba had given him, and Fionn with his people took leave and farewell of the Ri and of his household, and left them good wishes for life and health, and the Ri sent the same with the Fianna. Fionn and his company went their way, and no tidings are told of them until they reached the Brugh na Boyne, and he and his people went ashore. After that Fionn sent messengers to the house of Aonghus of the Brugh to proclaim battle against Diarmuid O'Duibhne.[3]

What shall I do about this, O Oscar?" said Diarmuid.

∾

[1] Either his seat or his place of honor.
[2] The Irish is *sluag*: a multitude, host, or army.
[3] *To proclaim battle*; that is, to challenge him.

"We will both of us give them battle, and destroy them, and rend their flesh, and not suffer a servant to escape alive of them, but we will slay them all," said Oscar.

Upon the morrow morning Diarmuid and Oscar rose, and harnessed their fair bodies in their suits of arms of valor and battle, and those two mighty heroes went their way to the place of that combat, and woe to those, either many or few, who might meet those two good warriors when in anger.

Then Diarmuid and Oscar bound the rims of their shields together so that they might not separate from one another in the fight. After that they proclaimed battle against Fionn, and then the children of the Ri of Alba said that they and their people would go to strive with them first. They came ashore immediately, and rushed to meet and to encounter them, and Diarmuid O'Duibhne passed under them, through them, and over them, as a hawk would go through small birds, or a whale through small fish, or a wolf through a large flock of sheep; and such was the dispersion and terror and scattering that those good warriors wrought upon the strangers, that not a man escaped them to tell tidings or to boast of great deeds, but all of them fell by Diarmuid and by Oscar before the night came, and they themselves were smooth and free from hurt, having neither cut nor wound.

When Fionn saw that great slaughter, he and his people returned back out to sea, and no tidings are told of them until they reached Tir Tairngire, where Fionn's nurse was. Fionn went before her after that, and she received him joyfully. Fionn told the cause of his travel and of his journey to the old woman from first to last, and the reason of his strife with Diarmuid O'Duibhne, and that it was to seek counsel from her that he was then come; also that no strength of a host or of a multitude could conquer Diarmuid, if by chance magic alone might not conquer him. "I will go with you," said the hag, "and I will practice magic against him." Fionn was joyful at that, and he remained with the hag that night; and they resolved to depart on the morrow.

Now it is not told how they fared until they reached the Brugh na Boyne, and the hag threw a spell of magic about Fionn and the Fianna, so that the men of Erin knew not that they were there. It was the day before that Oscar had parted from Diarmuid, and Diarmuid chanced to be hunting and chasing on the day that the hag concealed the Fianna. This was revealed to the hag, and she caused herself to fly by magic upon the leaf of a water lily,[1] having a hole in the middle of it, in the fashion of the quern-stone of a mill, so that she rose with the blast of the pure cold wind and came over Diarmuid, and began to aim at and strike him through the hole with deadly darts, so

∽

[1] This is the yellow water lily. Literally translated, the Irish in the text reads "the drowned leaf."

that she wrought the hero great hurt in the midst of his weapons and armor,[2] and that he was unable to escape, so greatly was he oppressed; and every evil that had ever come upon him was little compared to that evil. What he thought in his mind was that unless he might strike the hag through the hole that was in the leaf, she would cause his death upon the spot; and Diarmuid laid himself upon his back, having the Ga dearg in his hand, and made a triumphant cast of exceeding courage with the javelin, so that he reached the hag through the hole, and she fell dead upon the spot. Diarmuid beheaded her there and then, and took her head with him to Aonghus of the Brugh.

Diarmuid rose early on the morrow, and Aonghus rose and went where Fionn was, and asked him whether he would make peace with Diarmuid. Fionn said that he would, in whatever way Diarmuid would make peace. Then Aonghus went where the Ri of Erin was to ask peace for Diarmuid, and Cormac said that he would grant him that. Again Aonghus went where Diarmuid and Grainne were, and asked Diarmuid whether he would make peace with Cormac and with Fionn. Diarmuid said that he would if he obtained the conditions that he should ask of them.

"What are those conditions?" said Aonghus.

"The district," said Diarmuid, "which my father

≈

[2] Though protected by weapons and covered by armor, Diarmuid was still badly wounded.

had, that is, the district of O'Duibhne,[1] and that Fionn shall not hunt nor chase within it, and it must be free of rent or tribute to the Ri of Erin; also the district of Beann Damhuis,[2] that is, Dubhcharn in Leinster, as gifts for myself from Fionn, for they are the best districts in Erin; and the district of Ceis Corann[3] from the Ri of Erin as dowry with his daughter; and those are the conditions upon which I would make peace with them."

"Would you make peace on those conditions if you were to get them?" asked Aonghus.

"I could better bear to make peace by getting those conditions," said Diarmuid.

Then Aonghus went with those tidings to where the Ri of Erin and Fionn were, and he got those conditions from them every one, and they forgave Diarmuid all he had done as long as he had been outlawed, namely for the space of sixteen years; and Cormac gave his other daughter for wife and mate to Fionn, that he might let Diarmuid be, and so they made peace with each other; and the place that Diarmuid and Grainne

∾

[1] The present barony of Corca Ui Dhuibhne (Corcaguiney) in county Kerry.
[2] There is no barony in Leinster now bearing either of these names. *Beann Damhuis* means the peak of Damhus; perhaps this refers to the mountain called Dowse, corruptly pronounced Jowse, in county Wicklow.
[3] *Ceis Corainn.* The present barony of Corran, in county Sligo. The name is anglicised Keshcorran.

settled in was Rath[4] Ghrainne in the district of Ceis Corann, far from Fionn and from Cormac.

Then Grainne bore Diarmuid four sons and one daughter; namely, Donnchad, Eochaidh, Connla, Seil-bhshearcach, and Druime; and he gave the district of Beann Damhuis, that is, Dubhcharn in Leinster, to the daughter, and he sent a brughaidh, a biadhtach,[5] and a female attendant to serve her there. They abode a long time fulfilling the peace with each other, and people used to say that there was not living at the same time with him a man richer in gold and silver, in kine and cattle-herds and sheep, and who made more successful raids, than Diarmuid.[6]

Then Grainne spoke to Diarmuid upon a certain day, and what she said was that it was a shame for them, seeing the number of their people and the greatness

෴

[4] A rath is a circular compound, including house, outbuildings, and enclosing wall, common to the Irish warrior class.

[5] *Brughaidh* and *Biadhtach* were two kinds of farmers among the ancient Irish. The former, which were the most numerous, held their land subject to a rent, the latter rent free in return for which they were bound to entertain travelers and the soldiers of their chief on the march. For a fascinating and in-depth treatment of the farming classes in medieval Ireland, see Patterson's *Cattle Lords and Clansmen.*

[6] The Irish term for a raid or a preying is *creach*. An Irish ri was bound to make a creach into some neighboring territory as soon as possible after his inauguration, in order that the tribe might judge his qualities as a leader. Note that Diarmuid has, indeed, made the shift from fianna warrior to cattle lord.

of their household, and that their expenditure was untold, that the two best men in Erin had never been in their house, that is, Cormac mac Art, the Ard Ri of Erin, and Fionn mac Cumhaill.

"Why do you speak in that manner, O Grainne," said Diarmuid, "when they are enemies to me?"

"I would gladly," said Grainne, "give them a feast, so that you might win their love."

"I permit that," said Diarmuid.

"Then," said Grainne, "send word and messengers to your daughter to bid her to prepare another feast, so that we may take the Ri of Erin and Fionn mac Cumhaill to her house; and how do we know but that there she might get a fitting husband?"

Thereupon two great feasts were prepared by Grainne and by her daughter for the length of a year, and at the end of that space and season word and messengers were sent for the Ri of Erin, and for Fionn mac Cumhaill, and for the seven battalions of the standing Fianna, and for the chiefs of Erin likewise, and they were for a year from day to day enjoying that feast.

Now on the last day of the year[1] Diarmuid was in Rath Ghrainne asleep; and Diarmuid heard the voice of a hound in his sleep in the night, and that caused Diarmuid to start out of his sleep, so that Grainne

~

[1] That is Samain, October 31st, and perhaps also the last day of the feast.

caught him and threw her two arms about him, and asked him what he had seen. "It is the voice of a hound I have heard," said Diarmuid, "and I marvel to hear it in the night."

"May you be kept safely," said Grainne, "for it is the Tuatha De Danann that are doing that to you to spite Aonghus of the Brugh. Lay you down on your bed again." Nevertheless no slumber or sleep fell upon Diarmuid then, and he heard the voice of the hound again. Again that roused Diarmuid and he was eager to go to seek the hound. Grainne caught him and laid him down the second time, and told him it was not fitting for him to go look for a hound because of hearing its voice in the night. Diarmuid laid him upon his bed, and a heaviness of slumber and of sweet sleep fell upon him, and a third time the voice of the hound awoke him.

The day came then with its full light, and he said, "I will go to seek the hound whose voice I have heard, since it is day."

"Well then," said Grainne, "take with you the Moralltach, that is, the sword of Manannan, and the Ga dearg."

"I will not," said Diarmuid, "but I will take the Beag-alltach[2] and the Ga buidhe with me in my hand, and

~

[2] *Beag-alltach* translates as the small fierce one, a less powerful sword than that given to Diarmuid by Aonghus.

my hound Mac an Cull[1] by a chain in my other hand."

Then Diarmuid went forth from Rath Ghrainne, and did not halt until he reached the summit of Beann Gulbain,[2] and he found Fionn before him there without any one with him or in his company. Diarmuid gave him no greeting, but asked him whether it was he that was holding that chase.

Fionn said that it was not he, but that a company of the Fianna had risen out after midnight, "and one of our hounds came across the track of a wild pig, being loose by our side, so they have not yet been able to retake him. Now it is the wild boar of Beann Gulbain that the hound has met, and the Fianna do but uselessly follow him; for often before now he has escaped them, and thirty warriors of the Fianna were slain by him this morning. He is even now coming up against the mountain toward us, with the Fianna fleeing before him, and let us leave this hill to him." Diarmuid said that he would not leave the hill through fear of him.

"It is not proper for you to do thus," said Fionn, "for you are under geasa never to hunt a pig."

"Why were those geasa laid upon me?" said Diarmuid.

❧

[1] *Mac an Cull* translates as the son of hazel; this is Diarmuid's favorite hound.
[2] *Beann Gulbain* is a mountain in county Sligo, now corruptly called in English Benbulbin.

"That I will tell you," said Fionn. "On a certain day that I chanced to be in Almhuin the broad and great of Leinster, with the seven battalions of the standing Fianna about me, Bran beag O'Buadhchain came in and asked me whether I remembered not that it was one of my geasa not to be ten nights one after the other in Almhuin without being out of it for a single night. Now those geasa had not been laid upon any man of the Fianna but upon myself alone. The Fianna went into the great hall that night, and no man stayed by me but your father and a small number of the bards and learned men of the Fianna, with our staghounds and our other dogs.

"Then I asked of them who were with me where we should go to be entertained that night. Your father, that is, Donn O'Donnchudha, said that he would give me entertainment for that night, 'for if you remember, O Fionn,' said Donn, 'when I was outlawed and banished from you and from the Fianna, Crochnuit the daughter of Currach of Life became pregnant by me, and bore a smooth beautiful man-child of that heavy pregnancy, and Aonghus of the Brugh took that son from me to foster him. Crochnuit bore another son after that to Roc mac Diocain,[3] and Roc asked me to take that son to foster, seeing that Aonghus had my son, and he said that he would provide a sufficient meal for nine men

~

[3] *Roc mac Diocain* was the head steward to Aonghus.

at the house of Aonghus every evening. I said that I thought it not fitting to take the servant's son, and I sent to Aonghus praying him to receive that son to foster him. Aonghus received the servant's son, and there was not a time after that when Roc did not send a nine men's meal to the house of Aonghus for me. However, I have not seen him for a year, and we shall, as many as there are here of us, get entertainment for this night there.'

"I and Donn went our way after that," said Fionn, "to the house of Aonghus of the Brugh, and you were there that night, O Diarmuid, and Aonghus showed you great fondness. The son of the steward was your companion that night, and not greater was the fondness that Aonghus showed you than the fondness that the people of Aonghus showed the son of the steward, and your father suffered great envy for that.

"It was no long time after that that there arose a quarrel between two of my staghounds about some broken meat that was thrown them, and the women and the lesser people of the place fled before them, and the others rose to separate them. The son of the steward went between your father's knees, flying before the staghounds, and he gave the child a mighty, powerful, strong squeeze of his two knees, so that he killed him on the spot, and he cast him under the feet of the staghounds.

"Afterward the steward came and found his son dead, and he uttered a long very pitiful cry. Then he came before me, and what he said was, 'There is not in this house tonight a man that has got out of this uproar worse than myself, for I had no children but one son only, and he has been slain; and how shall I get repayment from you, O Fionn?'

"I told him to examine his son, and if he found the trace of a staghound's tooth or nail upon him that I would myself give him eric for him. The child was examined, and no trace of a staghound's tooth or nail was found on him.

"Then the steward laid me under dangerous geasa and destructive spells of druidism that I should show him who had slain his son. I asked for a fidchell board and water to be brought to me, and I washed my hands and put my thumb under my tooth of divination,[1] so that true and exact divination was shown me, namely, that your father had slain the son of the steward between his two knees. I offered eric myself when that was shown me, but the steward refused that; so that I was forced to tell him that it was your father that had slain his son.

"The steward said that there was not in the house a man for whom it was more easy to give eric than your father, for that he himself had a son at that place, and that he would not take any eric whatever except that

～

[1] In his youth Fionn touched his thumb to the Salmon of Knowledge and since then had had the gift of divination when he placed his thumb into his mouth in the manner described.

you should be placed between his two legs and his two knees, and that he would forgive the death of his son if he let you from him safe.

"Aonghus grew irate with the steward at that speech, and your father thought to take off his head, until I separated them. Then came the steward again with a magic wand of sorcery, and struck his son with that wand so that he made of him a cropped green pig, having neither ears or tail, and he said, 'I conjure you that you have the same length of life as Diarmuid O'Duibhne, and that it be by you that he shall fall at last.' Then the wild boar rose and stood, and rushed out by the open door. When Aonghus heard those spells laid upon you, he conjured you never to hunt a swine; and that wild boar is the wild boar of Beann Gulbain, and it is not fitting for you to await him upon this hill."

"I knew not of those geasa before now," said Diarmuid, "nor will I leave this hill through fear of him before he comes to me, and do you leave me your hound Bran beside Mac an Chuill."

"I will not," said Fionn, "for often this wild boar has escaped him before." Fionn went his way after that, and left Diarmuid alone and solitary upon the summit of the hill.

"By my word," said Diarmuid, "it is to slay me that you have made this hunt, O Fionn; and if it be here I am fated to die I have no power now to shun it."

The wild boar then came up the face of the mountain with the Fianna after him. Diarmuid slipped

Mac an Chuill from his leash against him, and that profited him nothing, for he did not await the wild boar but fled before him. Diarmuid said, "Woe to him that heeds not the counsel of a good wife, for Grainne bade me at early morn today take with me the Moralltach and the Ga dearg." Then Diarmuid put his small white-colored ruddy-nailed finger into the silken string of the Ga buidhe, and made a careful cast at the pig, so that he smote him in the fair middle of his face and of his forehead; nevertheless he cut not a single bristle upon him, nor did he give him wound or scratch. Diarmuid's courage was lessened at that, and thereupon he drew the Beag-alltach from the sheath in which it was kept, and struck a heavy stroke upon the wild boar's back stoutly and bravely, yet he cut not a single bristle upon him, but made two pieces of his sword.

Then the wild boar made a fearless spring upon Diarmuid, so that he tripped him and made him fall headlong, and when he rose up again it happened that one of his legs was on either side of the wild boar, and his face looking backward toward the hind part of the wild boar. The wild boar fled down the fall of the hill and was unable to throw off Diarmuid during that space. After that he fled away until he reached Eas ruaidh[1] mhic Bhadhairn, and having reached the

‿

[1] *Eas ruaidh* translates as the red waterfall. It has been identified as Assaroe Falls, near Ballyshannon in county Donegal.

red stream he gave three nimble leaps across the fall, from one side to the other and back and forth, yet he could not put off Diarmuid during that space; and he came back by the same path, until he reached up to the height of the mountain again. And when he had reached the top of the hill he threw Diarmuid from his back; and when he was fallen to the earth the wild boar made an eager, exceeding mighty spring upon him, and ripped out his bowels and his entrails so that they fell about his legs.

However, as the boar was leaving the hill, Diarmuid made a triumphant cast of the hilt of the sword that chanced to be still in his hand, so that he dashed out the boar's brains and left him dead without life. Therefore Rath na h-Amhrann[1] is the name of the place that is on the top of the mountain from that time to this.

It was no long time after that when Fionn and the Fianna of Erin came up, and the agonies of death and of instant dissolution were then coming upon Diarmuid.

"It likes me well to see you in that plight, O Diarmuid," said Fionn; "and I grieve that all the women of Erin are not now gazing upon you: for your excellent beauty is turned to ugliness, and your choice form to deformity."

"Nevertheless it is in your power to heal me, O

⁓

[1] *Rath na h-Amhrann* translates as the rath or barrow of the sword hilt.

Fionn," said Diarmuid, "if it were your pleasure to do so."

"How should I heal you?" said Fionn.

"Easily," said Diarmuid; "for when you received the noble precious gift of divining at the Boyne, it was given to you that to whomever you should give a drink from the palms of your hands he should after that be young and sound from any sickness he might have at that time."

"You have not deserved of me that I should give you that drink," said Fionn.

"That is not true," said Diarmuid, "well have I deserved it of you; for when you went to the house of Dearc the son of Donnarthadh, and the chiefs and great nobles of Erin with you, to enjoy a banquet and feast, Cairbre Liffeachair son of Cormac son of Art and the men of Mag Breagh, and of Mide, and of Cearmna, and the stout mighty pillars of Teamhair came around the stronghold against you, and uttered three shouts loudly about you, and threw fire and firebrands into it. At that you rose and stood, and would have gladly gone out; but I bade you stay within enjoying drinking and pleasure, and that I would myself go out to avenge it upon them. Then I went out and quenched the flames, and made three deadly courses about the stronghold, so that I slew fifty at each course, and came in having no cut nor wound by them. And you were cheerful, joyous, and of good courage before me that night, O Fionn," said

Diarmuid; "and had it been that night that I asked you for a drink, you would have given it to me, and you would not have done so more justly that night than now."

"That is not true," said Fionn; "you have ill deserved of me that I should give you a drink or do you any good thing; for the night that you went with me to Teamhair you bore away Grainne from me in the presence of all the men of Erin when you were yourself my guard over her in Teamhair that night."

"The guilt of that was not mine, O Fionn," said Diarmuid, "but Grainne put a geis upon me, and I would not have failed to keep my geasa for the gold of the world, and nothing, O Fionn, is true of all that you say, for you would acknowledge that I have well deserved that you should give me a drink, if you remembered the night that Miodhach the son of Colgan made you the feast of Bruighean an Chaorthainn.[1] He had a stronghold upon land, and a stronghold upon an island, and he brought the Ri of the World and the three Rioga of Innis Tuile to the stronghold that he had upon the wave, with intent to take your head

∾

[1] According to the romance of *Bruighean an Chaorthainn*, or the enchanted fort of the quicken tree, Colgan was Ri of Lochlin (Scandanavia). He invaded Ireland because he considered his hereditary title, "Ri of the Isles," an empty title, seeing that he no longer possessed all the islands of the north Atlantic as his ancestors had done, Ireland having been taken back by the Irish.

from you. The feast was being given in the stronghold that he had on land, and he sent and asked you and the seven battalions of the standing Fianna to go and enjoy the feast in Bruigheann an Chaorthainn. Now you went and certain of the chiefs of the Fianna together with you, to enjoy that banquet in Bruigheann an Chaorthainn, and Miodhach caused the mold of Innis Tuile to be placed under you, so that your feet and your hands stuck to the ground; and when the Ri of the World heard that you were thus bound down, he sent a chief of a hundred to seek your head. Then you did put your thumb under your tooth of divination, and knowledge and enlightenment was shown you.

"At that very time I came after you to Bruigheann an Chaorthainn, and you knew me as I came to the stronghold, and made known to me that the Ri of the World and the three Rioga of Innis Tuile were in the stronghold of the island upon the Siona[2] and that it would not be long before some one would come from them to seek your head and take it to the Ri of the World. When I heard that, I took the protection of your body and of your life upon me till the dawning of the day on the morrow, and I went to the ford which was by the stronghold to defend it.[3]

"I had not been long by the ford before there came

∼

[2] *Siona*, the Shannon river.
[3] The fort was approached by a ford.

a chief of a hundred to me of the people of the Ri of the World, and we fought together; and I took his head from him, and made slaughter of his people, and brought the head even to the stronghold of the island where the Ri of the World was enjoying drinking and pleasure with the three Rioga of Innis Tuile by him. I took their heads from them, and put them in the hollow of my shield, and brought in my left hand the jewelled golden-chased goblet, full of old mead, pleasant to drink, which was before the Ri. Then I wrought sharply with my sword around me, and came by virtue of my fortune and of my valor to Bruighean an Chaorthainn, and brought those heads with me. I gave you the goblet in token of slaughter,[1] and rubbed the blood of those three Rioga on you and on the Fianna, as many of them as were bound, so that I restored to you your power over the vigor of your hands and the motion of your feet; and had I asked a drink of you that night, O Fionn, I would have got it!

"Many is the strait, moreover, that has overtaken you and the Fianna of Erin from the first day that I came among you, in which I have risked my body and my life for your sake; and therefore you should not do me this foul treachery. Moreover, many a brave warrior and valiant hero of great prowess has fallen by

∽

[1] A *token of slaughter* means a token of victory.

you, nor is there an end of them yet; and shortly there will come a dire disaster upon the Fianna which will not leave them many descendants.[2] Nor is it for you that I grieve, O Fionn, but for Oisin, and for Oscar, and for the rest of my faithful, fond comrades. And as for you, O Oisin, you shall be left to lament after the Fianna, and you shall sorely lack me yet, O Fionn."

Then said Oscar, "O Fionn, though I am more nearly akin to you than to Diarmuid O'Duibhne, I will not suffer you to withhold the drink from Diarmuid; and I swear, moreover, that were any other prince in the world to do Diarmuid O'Duibhne such treachery, there should only escape whichever of us should have the strongest hand, and bring him a drink without delay."

"I know no well whatever upon this mountain," said Fionn.

"That is not true," said Diarmuid; "for but nine paces from you is the best well of pure water in the world."

After that Fionn went to the well, and raised the full of his two hands of the water; but he had not reached more than half way to Diarmuid when he let the water run down through his hands, and he said he could not bring the water.

∾

[2] Diarmuid prophesied correctly, for the Fenians were crushed at the Battle of Gabhra and Oisin did indeed live on for many generations, reciting the tales of the Fianna.

"I swear," said Diarmuid, "that of your own will you did let it run from your hands."

Fionn went for the water a second time, and he had not come more than the same distance when he let it through his hands, having thought upon Grainne. Then Diarmuid heaved a piteous sigh of anguish when he saw that.

"I swear upon my arms," said Oscar, "that if you bring not the water speedily, O Fionn, there shall not leave this hill but either you or I." Fionn returned to the well a third time because of that speech which Oscar had made to him, and brought the water to Diarmuid, and as he came up the life parted from the body of Diarmuid.

Then that company of the Fianna of Erin that were present raised three great exceeding loud shouts, wailing for Diarmuid O'Duibhne, and Oscar looked fiercely and wrathfully upon Fionn and what he said was, "It is a greater pity that Diarmuid should be dead than it would have been had you perished, and the Fianna has lost their yoke of battle[1] by means of you."

Fionn then said, "Let us leave this hill, for fear that Aonghus of the Brugh and the Tuatha De Danann might catch us; and though we have no part in the slaying of Diarmuid, he would none the more readily believe us."

⁓

[1] *Yoke of battle*. The warrior who kept them together, their mainstay.

"I swear," said Oscar, "had I known that it was with intent to kill Diarmuid that you made the hunt of Beann Gulbain, that you would never have made it."

Then Fionn and the Fianna of Erin went their way from the hill, Fionn holding Diarmuid's staghound, that is Mac an Chuill, but Oisin, and Oscar, and Caoilte, and the son of Lughaidh returned back, and threw their four mantles about Diarmuid, and after that they went their way after Fionn.

It is not told how they fared until they reached Rath Ghrainne, and Grainne was before them out upon the ramparts of the rath, so that she saw Fionn and the Fianna of Erin coming to her. Then said Grainne, "If Diarmuid were alive it would not be by Fionn that Mac an Chuill would be held coming to this place." Now Grainne was at that time heavy and pregnant, and she fell out over the ramparts of the rath, and brought forth three dead sons upon the spot.

When Oisin saw Grainne in that plight he sent away Fionn and the Fianna of Erin; and as Fionn and the Fianna of Erin were leaving the place Grainne lifted up her head and asked Fionn to leave her Mac an Chuill. He said that he would not give him to her, and that he thought it not too much that he himself should inherit so much of the son of O'Duibhne; but when Oisin heard that he took the staghound from the hand of Fionn, gave him to Grainne, and then followed his people.

Then Grainne felt certain of the death of Diarmuid,

and she uttered a long exceedingly piteous cry, so that it was heard in the distant parts of the rath; and her women and the rest of her people came to her, and asked her what had thrown her into that excessive grief. Grainne told them how Diarmuid had perished by the wild boar of Beann Gulbain, by means of the hunt that Fionn mac Cumhaill had made. "And truly my very heart is grieved," said Grainne, "that I am not myself able to fight with Fionn, for were I so I would not have suffered him to leave this place in safety." Having heard that, the death of Diarmuid, they too uttered three loud, fearful, vehement cries together with Grainne, so that those loud shouts were heard in the clouds of heaven, and in the wastes of the firmament; and then Grainne bade the five hundred that she had for household to go to Beann Gulbain, and to bring her the body of Diarmuid.

At that very time and season it was shown to Aonghus that Diarmuid was dead upon Beann Gulbain (for he had had no watch over him the night before), and he proceeded, accompanying the pure cold wind, so that he reached Beann Gulbain at the same time as the people of Grainne; and when Grainne's household recognized Aonghus they held out the rough side[1] of their shields in token of peace, and Aonghus

---

[1] *The rough side* is the wrong side, or inside, the shield being made of wood or wicker work covered outside with leather.

knew them. Then when they were met together upon
Beann Gulbain, they and the people of Aonghus raised
three exceeding great terrible cries over the body of
Diarmuid, so that they were heard in the clouds of
heaven, and in the wastes of the firmament of the air,
and in the provinces of Erin likewise.

Then Aonghus spoke, and what he said was, "It has
never been for one night, since I took you with me to
the Brugh na Boyne, at the age of nine months, that
I did not watch you and carefully keep you against
your foes, until last night, O Diarmuid O'Duibhne!
and alas for the treachery that Fionn has done you,
notwithstanding that you were at peace with him."
And he sang the following lay:

> Alas, O Diarmuid O'Duibhne,
> O thou of the white teeth, thou bright and fair one;
> Alas for thine own blood upon thy spear,
> The blood of thy body hath been shed.
>
> Alas for the deadly flashing tusk of the boar,
> Thou hast been sharply, sorely, violently lopped off
> By the malicious, fickle, treacherous,
> Dragging, stoutly great, vicious gapped one.[2]

---

[2] This line was wanting in all copies that O'Grady had seen, and
he left it blank, remarking that it and the previous line referred
to Fionn. The line is complete in Shéaghdha's edition and clearly refers to the boar.

Numb venom hath entered his wounds,
At Rath Fhinn he met his death;
The Boar of Beann Gulbain with fierceness,
Hath laid low Diarmuid the bright-faced.

Raise ye fairy shouts without gainsaying,
Let Diarmuid of the bright weapons be lifted by you;
To the smooth Brugh of the everlasting rocks —
Surely it is we that feel great pity.

After that lay Aonghus asked the household of Grainne why they were come to that spot. They said Grainne had sent them for the body of Diarmuid to bring it to her to Rath Ghrainne. Aonghus said that he would not let them take Diarmuid's body, but that he would himself bear it to the Brugh na Boyne; "And since I cannot restore him to life I will send a soul into him, so that he may talk to me each day." After that Aonghus caused the body to be borne upon a gilded bier, with Diarmuid's javelins over him pointed upwards, and he went his way until he reached the Brugh na Boyne.

As for Grainne's household, they returned back to Rath Ghrainne, and they told how Aonghus would not let them bring the body of Diarmuid, but that he himself had taken it to the Brugh na Boyne; and Grainne said that she had no power over him.

The Body of Diarmuid

Afterwards Grainne sent word and messengers for her children to the district of Corca Ui Duibhne, where they were being reared and protected. Now those children of Diarmuid each had a Biadhtach, and sons of Oglachs and of Brughaidhs serving them, and each son of them owned a district.[1] Now Donnchadh the son of Diarmuid O'Duibhne was the eldest son of them, and to him the other sons were subject; that is, Eochaid, Connla, Seilbhshearcach, and Ollann the long-bearded, the son of Diarmuid, that is, the son of the daughter of the Ri of Leinster; and Grainne bore greater love and affection to none of her own children than to Ollann.

Those messengers thereupon went their way until they reached the place where those youths were, and they told them the cause of their journey and of their coming from first to last; and as the youths were setting out with the full number of their household and of their gathering, their friends asked them what they should do since their lords were now going to encounter war and perilous adventure against Fionn mac Cumhaill and the Fianna of Erin. Donnchadh the son of Diarmuid bade them abide in their own places, and that if they made peace with Fionn their people need fear nothing; and if not, to choose which lord they would have, that is, to side with Fionn or to adhere to their own chiefs as they pleased.

And no tidings are told of them until they reached Rath Ghrainne, where Grainne gave them a gentle welcome, and gave a kiss and a welcome to the son of

∾

[1] *Biadhtach, Oglach, Brughaidh. Biadhtach* and *Brughaidh* were two kinds of farmers, as explained in the note on p. 133. An *Oglach* was a youthful retainer or attendant.

the daughter of the Ri of Leinster; and they entered together into Rath Ghrainne, and sat at the sides of the royal stronghold according to their rank, and their patrimony, and according to the age of each one of them, and there were given them mead mild and pleasant to drink, and well-prepared very sweet ale, and strong fermented draughts in fair chased drinking horns, so that they became intoxicated and mirthful. And then Grainne spoke with an exceeding loud and clear voice, and what she said was, "O dear children, your father has been slain by Fionn mac Cumhaill against his bonds and covenants of peace with him; and you must avenge that upon him well; and there stands your portion of the inheritance of your father," said she, "that is, his arms, and his armor, and his various sharp weapons, and his feats of valor and of bravery likewise. I will myself portion them out among you, and may the getting of them bring you success in battle. And I myself will have the goblets, and the drinking horns, and the beautiful golden-chased cups, and the kine and the cattle-herds undivided." And she sang this lay as follows:

> Arise ye, O children of Diarmuid,
> Go forth and learn that I may see;
> May your adventure be prosperous to you;
> The tidings of a good man have come to you.[2]

~

[2] Meaning, "You have heard the fame of your brave father."

The sword for Donnchadh,
The best son that Diarmuid had;
And let Eochaid have the Ga dearg;
They lead to every advantage.

Give his armor from me to Ollann,
Safe every body upon which it may be put;
And his shield to Connla,
To him that keeps the battalions firm.

The goblets and the drinking horns,
The cups and the bowls,
They are a woman's treasure without thanks;
I alone shall have them all.

Slay ye women and children,
Through hatred to your foes;
Do no guile nor treachery,
Hasten ye and depart. Arise.

After that lay Grainne bade them depart and learn carefully all practice of bravery and of valor till they should have reached their full strength, and to spend a portion of their time with Bolcan, that is, the smith of hell.[1]

Then those good youths began their journey, and they took farewell of Grainne and of her household,

∽

[1] *Bolcan* is Vulcan. The name is adapted to the Irish alphabet and pronunciation.

and left them wishes for life and health, and Grainne and her people sent the same with them; and they left not a warrior, a hero, nor a woman-warrior in the distant regions of the world with whom they spent not a portion of their time, learning from them until they attained fullness of strength; and they were three years with Bolcan.

When Fionn was assured that those children of Diarmuid had departed upon that journey, he became filled with hatred and great fear of them, and without delay mustered the seven battalions of the standing Fianna from every quarter where they were; and when they were come to one place Fionn told them with a loud, bright-clear voice the history of that journey of the children of Diarmuid O'Duibhne from first to last, and asked what he should do in the matter. "For it is with intent to rebel against me," said he, "that they are gone upon that journey."

Oisin spoke, and what he said was, "The guilt of that is no man's but yours, and we will not support the deed that we have not done, and foul is the treachery that you did show toward Diarmuid O'Duibhne, though at peace with him, when Cormac also would have given you his other daughter in order that you might bear Diarmuid no enmity nor malice. According as you have planted the oak so bend it yourself." Fionn was grieved at those words of Oisin; nevertheless he could do nothing against him.

When Fionn saw that Oisin, and Oscar, and all the

Clanna Baoisgne had abandoned him, he considered within his own mind that he would be unable to crush that danger if he did not win over Grainne; and therefore he went to Rath Ghrainne without the knowledge of the Fianna of Erin and without bidding them farewell, and greeted her craftily, and cunningly, and with sweet words.

Grainne neither heeded nor hearkened to him, but told him to leave her sight, and straightway assailed him with her keen, very sharp-pointed tongue. However, Fionn left not plying her with sweet words and with gentle loving discourse, until he brought her to his own will; and he had the desire of his heart and soul of her.

After that Fionn and Grainne set out on their way, and no tidings are told of them until they reached the Fianna of Erin; and when the Fianna saw Fionn and Grainne coming toward them in that fashion, they gave one shout of derision and mockery at her, so that Grainne bowed her head through shame.

"We trust, O Fionn," said Oisin, "that you will keep Grainne well from henceforth."

As for the children of Diarmuid, after having spent seven years in learning all that befits a warrior, they came out of the far regions of the great world, and it is not told how they fared until they reached Rath Ghrainne. When they had heard how Grainne had fled with Fionn mac Cumhaill without taking leave of them or of the Ri of Erin, they said that they could do nothing. After that they went to Almhuin of Leinster to seek Fionn and the Fianna, and they proclaimed battle against Fionn.

"Rise, O Diorruing, and ask them how many they require," said Fionn. Then Diorruing went and asked them.

"We require a hundred men against each of us, or single combat," said they. Fionn sent a hundred to fight with them, and when they had reached the place of battle those youths rushed under them, through them, and over them, and made three heaps of them, namely, a heap of their heads, a heap of their bodies, and a heap of their arms and armor. "Our hosts will not last," said Fionn, "if a hundred be slain each day. What shall we do concerning those youths, O Grainne?"

"I will go to them," said Grainne, "to try whether I may be able to make peace between you."

"I should be well pleased at that," said Fionn, "and I would give them and their posterity freedom forever, and their father's place among the Fianna, and bonds and securities for the fulfillment thereof to them forever and ever."

Grainne went to meet them, gave them a welcome, and made them those offers. At last Grainne made peace between them, and those bonds and securities were given to them, and they got their father's place among the Fianna from Fionn mac Cumhaill. After that a banquet and feast was prepared for them, so that they became intoxicated and mirthful. And Fionn and Grainne stayed by one another until they died.

Thus far, then, the Pursuit of Diarmuid and Grainne.[1]

∽

[1] Such is the invariable ending of an Irish story. This closing sentence is very useful in closely written manuscripts where stories are crowded together, often without heading, for determining where one tract ends and the next begins.

Introduction

The Exile of the Sons of Uisliu belongs to the Ulster cycle, which predates much of the Fenian cycle by several hundred years. An earlier prototype of the story told in *The Pursuit of Diarmuid and Grainne*, it achieves striking emotional effect through its sections of compact verse and its distressing conclusion.

The tale has been translated into English many times and there are good introductions to the story by Hull, Kinsella, and Gantz.[1] The current text is a modernization of the 1905 translation by A. H. Leahy.

[1] Vernam Hull, *Longes Mac N-Uislenn: The Exile of the Sons of Uisliu* (New York, 1949); Thomas Kinsella, *The Tain* (Oxford, 1970); and Jeffrey Gantz, *Early Irish Myths and Sagas* (New York, 1981).

The Exile of the Sons of Uisliu

In the house of Feidlimid mac Dall, who was the storyteller of Conchobur, the men of Ulaid[2] sat at their ale; and attending them was the wife of Feidlimid, and she was great with child. Around the house went drinking-horns, and portions of food; and the revellers shouted in their drunken mirth. And when the men desired to sleep, the woman also went to her bed; and as she passed through the house, the child cried out in her womb, so that its shriek was heard throughout the house, and throughout the rath.[3] And upon that shriek, all the men sprang up; and chin to chin they jostled throughout the house. At this Sencha, the son of Ailill, rebuked them: "Let none of you stir!" cried he, "and let the woman be brought before us that we may learn the meaning of that cry."

Then they brought the woman before them, and Feidlimid, her husband, spoke to her:

What is that, of all cries far the fiercest,
In your womb raging loudly and long?
You pierce all ears with that clamor;
With that scream, from a dwelling swollen and strong.

∾

[2] *Ulaid* is the Old Irish name for Ulster.
[3] A *rath* is a circular compound, including house, outbuildings, and enclosing wall, common to the Irish warrior class.

Of great woe, for that cry, is my heart foreboding,
Torn through with terror, and sore with the hurt.

Then the woman turned and approached Cathbad
the Druid, for he was a man of knowledge, and spoke
to him thus:

Let Cathbad hear, the fair one,
With face that all love,
The prince, the royal diadem,
Let he who is extolled be increased
By druid arts of the druid;
I have no words of wisdom
To answer to Feidlimid,
No light of knowledge;
For the nature of woman is not to know
What she bears, or what
In the hollow of her womb cries out.

And then said Cathbad:

’Tis a maid who screamed wildly so lately;
Fair and curling locks shall round her flow;
Stately eyes of blue she will have;
Her cheeks shall glow like the foxglove.

Wondrous her skin in its whiteness,
The color of new snow;
Her teeth are faultless in splendor;
Her lips are scarlet red.

A fair woman for whom Ulaid's chariot heroes
Shall fight and die;
A woman that gave that shriek,
Golden-haired, with long tresses, and tall.

For whose love many chiefs will strive,
And great rioga[1] will call for her favors.
To the west she will hasten, beguiling
A great host, that will steal from the Ulaid.

Scarlet red her lips shall be smiling,
Revealing her teeth, white as pearls:
Yes, that woman is fair. Great queens shall
Covet her form, faultless and unflawed.

Then Cathbad laid his hand upon the body of the woman; and the little child moved beneath his hand. "Yes, indeed," he said, "it is a woman child who is here. Deirdre shall be her name, and evil woe shall be upon her."

Now some days after that the girl child was born, and then Cathbad sang:

Deirdre, great cause of destruction,
Though thou art fair of face and famous,

∽

[1] *Ri* (pl. *rioga*) is the Irish term for king. Although details are complex, Irish rioga were normally elected; they did not inherit the position.

165

Ulaid shall sorrow in thy time,
Thou hidden daughter of Feidlimid.

Mischief there shall yet be afterwards
On your account, O brightly shining woman,
Hear this! At that time shall be
The exile of the three lofty sons of Uisliu.

It is in your time that a violent deed
Shall be done thereupon in Emain;
Yet afterwards shall it repent the violation
Of the safeguard of the mighty son of Roich.

It is through you, O woman with excellence,
The exile of Fergus from the Ulaid,
And a deed from which weeping will come,
The wound of Fiachna, the son of Conchobur.

It is thy fault, O woman with excellence,
The wound of Gerrc son of Illadan,
And a deed of no smaller importance,
The slaying of Eogan mac Durthacht.

You will do a deed that is wild and hateful
For wrath against the Ri of the noble Ulaid;
Your little grave shall be in that place,
Your tale shall be renowned, O Deirdre.

"Let that maiden be slain!" cried the young men of
Ulaid, but "Not so!" said Conchobur. "In the morning
she will be brought to me, and will be reared according

to my will, and she will be my wife, and in my companionship will she dwell."

The men of Ulaid were not so hardy as to turn Conchobur from his purpose, and so it was done. Deirdre was reared in a house that belonged to Conchobur, and she grew up to be the fairest woman in all Ireland. She was brought up at a distance from Emain Macha; so that none of the men of Ulaid might see her till the time came when she was to share the royal bed. No man was permitted to enter the house where she was reared, save only her foster father, and her foster mother, and in addition to these Lebarcham, who was a satirist and could not be refused.

Now it chanced upon a certain day in the time of winter that the foster-father of Deirdre had employed himself in skinning a calf upon the snow, in order to prepare a roast for her, and the blood of the calf lay upon the snow, and she saw a black raven who came down to drink it.

"Lebarcham," said Deirdre, "that man only will I love, who has the three colors that I see here, his hair as black as the raven, his cheeks red like the blood, and his body as white as the snow."

"Dignity and good fortune to thee!" said Lebarcham. "That man is not far away. He is nigh in the nearby rath; and the name of him is Noisiu, the son of Uisliu."

"I shall never be in good health again," said Deirdre, "until the time comes when I may see him."

It befell that Noisiu was upon a certain day alone

upon the rampart of Emain Macha, and he sent his warrior-cry with music abroad. Well did the musical cry ring out that was raised by the sons of Uisliu. Each cow and every beast that heard them gave two-thirds more milk than usual; and each man who heard that cry deemed it to be fully joyous, and a dear pleasure to him.

Skillful was the play of weapons by the three sons of Uisliu. If the whole province of Ulaid had been assembled against them in one place, and they three only had been able to set their backs against one another, the men of Ulaid would not have defeated those three, so well were they skilled in parry and defence. And they were swift of foot when they hunted game, and it was their custom to chase the quarry to its death.

Now when Noisiu found himself alone on the plain, Deirdre also soon escaped outside her house to him, and she ran past him, and at first he did not know who she might be.

"Fair is the young heifer that springs past me!" he cried.

"Well may the young heifers be great," she said, "in a place where none may find a bull."

"You have as your bull," said he, "the bull of the whole province of Ulaid, even Conchobur the Ri of the Ulaid."

"I would choose between you two," she said, "and I would take for myself a younger bull, even such as you are."

"Not so," said Noisiu, "for I fear the prophecy of Cathbad."

"Do you say this in order to refuse me?" said she.

"Yes indeed," he said; and she sprang upon him, and she seized him by his two ears. "Two ears of shame and of mockery you shall have," she cried, "if you do not take me with you."

"Release me, O my wife!" said he.

"That I will."

Then Noisiu raised his musical warrior-cry, and the men of Ulaid heard it, and each of them one after another sprang up; and the sons of Uisliu hurried out in order to hold back their brother.

"Why is it," they said, "that you do this? Let it not be through any fault of yours that war is stirred up between us and the men of Ulaid."

Then he told them all that had been done; and they said, "Evil will come on you from this; moreover you will lie under the reproach of shame so long as you live; but still we will go with her into another land, for there is no ri in all Ireland who will refuse us welcome if we come to him."

Then they took counsel together, and that same night they departed, three times fifty warriors, and the same number of women, and dogs, and servants, and Deirdre went with them. And for a long time they wandered about Ireland, in service to this man or that; and often Conchobur sought to slay them, either

by ambush or by treachery. From round about Eas
ruaidh[1] mhic Bhadhairn in the west they journeyed,
and they turned them back to Beinn Etair[2] in the
northeast.

Nevertheless the men of Ulaid drove them from
the land, and they came to the land of Alba,[3] and in
its wildernesses they dwelled. And when the chase
of the wild beasts of the mountains failed them, they
made foray upon the cattle of the men of Alba, and
took them for themselves; and the men of Alba gathered themselves together with intent to destroy them.

So then they took shelter with the Ri of Alba, and
the Ri took them into his following, and they served
him in war. And they made for themselves houses of
their own in the meadows by the Ri's rath. It was on
account of Deirdre that these houses were made, for
they feared that men might see her, and that on her
account they might be slain.

Now one day the high-steward of the Ri went out
in the early morning, and he looked about and into
Noisiu's house, and saw those two sleeping within,
and he hurried back to the Ri, and awakened him:
"We have," said he, "up to this day found no wife

∽

[1] *Eas ruaidh* translates as the red waterfall. Identified as Assaroe
Falls, near Ballyshannon in county Donegal.
[2] *Beinn Etair*, the Ben of Howth, is a mountain on the headland
of Howth, north of Dublin.
[3] *Alba* is northern Scotland.

for you of like dignity to yourself. Noisiu the son of Uisliu has a wife of worth sufficient for the emperor of the western world! Let Noisiu be slain, and let his wife share your bed."

"Not so!" said the Ri, "but prepare yourself to go each day to her house, and woo her for me secretly."

Thus was it done; but Deirdre, whatsoever the steward told her, was accustomed straightway to recount it each evening to her spouse; and since nothing was obtained from her, the sons of Uisliu were sent into dangers, and into wars, and into strifes that thereby they might be killed. Nevertheless they showed themselves to be stout in every strife, so that no advantage was gained by the Ri through such attempts.

The men of Alba were gathered together to destroy the sons of Uisliu, and this also was told to Deirdre. And she told her news to Noisiu: "Depart hence!" said she, "for if you depart not this night, upon the morrow you shall be slain!" And they marched away that night, and they went to an island of the sea.

Now the news of what had passed was brought to the men of Ulaid. "'Tis pity, O Conchobur!" said they, "that the sons of Uisliu should die in the land of foes for the sake of an evil woman. It is better that they should come under your protection, and that they should come into their own land, rather than that they should fall at the hands of foes."

"Let them come to us then," said Conchobur, "and

let men go as securities to them." The news was brought to them.

"This is welcome news for us," they said. "We will indeed come, and let Fergus come as our surety, and Dubthach, and Cormac the son of Conchobur." These then went to them, and they pursuaded them to pass over the sea.

But at the contrivance of Conchobur, Fergus was pressed to join in an ale-feast, while the sons of Uisliu were pledged to eat no food in Erin until they had eaten the food of Conchobur.[1] So Fergus tarried behind with Dubthach and Cormac; and the sons of Uisliu went on, accompanied by Fiacha, Fergus' son, until they came to the meadows around Emain.

Now at that time Eogan the son of Durthacht had come to Emain to make his peace with Conchobur, for they had for a long time been at enmity; and to him, and to the war-men of Conchobur, the charge was given that they should slay the sons of Uisliu, in order that they should not come before the Ri.

The sons of Uisliu stood upon the level part of the meadows, and the women sat upon the ramparts of Emain. And Eogan came with his warriors across

～

[1] A later version of the tale explains that Fergus has a *geis* that requires him to attend any ale-feast to which he is invited. Conchobur knows this and has treacherously manufactured the invitation. See Hull, *Longes Mac N-Uislenn* (New York, 1949) 115.

the meadow, and the son of Fergus took his place by Noisiu's side. And Eogan greeted them with a mighty thrust of his spear, and the spear broke asunder Noisiu's back and passed through it. The son of Fergus made a spring, and he threw both arms around Noisiu, and he brought him beneath himself to shelter him, while he threw himself down above him; and it was thus that Noisiu was slain, through the body of the son of Fergus.

Then there began a murder throughout the meadow, so that none escaped who did not fall by the points of the spears, or the edge of the sword, and Deirdre was brought to Conchobur to be in his power, and her arms were bound behind her back.

Now the sureties who had remained behind heard what had been done, even Fergus, and Dubthach, and Cormac. And then they hastened forward, and immediately performed great deeds. Dubthach killed, with the one thrust of his spear, Mane a son of Conchobur, and Fiachna the son of Feidelm, Conchobur's daughter; and Fergus struck down Traigthren, the son of Traiglethan, and his brother. And Conchobur was greatly angered at this, and he came to the fight with them; so that on that day three hundred of the men of Ulaid fell and Dubthach slew the women of Ulaid; and, before the day dawned, Fergus set Emain on fire.

Then they went away into exile, and went to the land of Connacht to find shelter with Ailill and Maeve, for they knew that that royal pair would give them good entertainment. To the men of Ulaid the exiles showed no love. Three thousand stout men went with them, and for sixteen years never did they allow cries of lamentation and of fear among the Ulaid to cease. Each night their vengeful forays caused men to quake and to wail.

Deirdre lived on for a year in the household of Conchobur, and during all that time she smiled no smile of laughter. She did not satisfy herself with food or with sleep, and she raised not her head from her knee. And if anyone brought entertainers before her, she used to speak thus:

> Though fair to you seems the keen band of heroes
> Who march into Emain that they lately left,
> More stately was the return to their home
> Of the three heroic sons of Uisliu.
>
> Noisiu, with mead of delicious hazel-nuts,
> Came to be bathed by me at the fire,
> Ardan, with an ox or boar of excellence,
> Aindle, a faggot on his stately back.
>
> Though sweet be the excellent mead to you
> Which is drunk by the son of Ness, the rich in strife,
> Before now I have known, leaping over a bank,
> Frequent sustenance much sweeter.

The Sons of Uisliu

When the noble Noisiu spread out
Cooking-hearth on the hero quarter of the wood,
Sweeter than any food dressed under honey
Was that captured by the son of Uisliu.

Though melodious to you seem
The pipers and horn-blowers,
It is my open statement to you today:
I have heard melody sweeter far than these.

For Conchobur, the Ri, are melody
Pipers and blowers of horns;
More melodious to me, renowned, enchanting,
The voice given out by the sons of Uisliu.

Like the sound of the wave the voice of Noisiu,
It was a melodious sound, one to hearken to forever,
Ardan was a good baritone,
The tenor of Aindle rang through the dwelling-place.

Noisiu is laid in his tomb;
Sad was the protection that he got;
The nation by which he was reared poured out
The cup of poison by which he died.

Beloved the hair of beautiful yellow,
Comely is the man, a great delight;
It is sorrowful that today I rise not
To await the sons of Uisliu.

THE EXILE OF

Dear the mind, firm, upright,
Dear the youth, lofty, modest;
After going with him through the dark wood,
Dear the girding at early morning.

Dear his gray eye, which women loved;
It was evil-looking against enemies;
After circuit of the wood was a noble assembly;
Dear the tenor through the dark wood.

I sleep not therefore,
And I stain not my nails with red;
Joy comes not to my wakefulness,
For the son of Tindell[1] does not return.

I do not sleep now,
For half the night on my bed;
My mind wanders amidst clouds of thoughts;
I do not eat, nor smile.

There is no leisure or joy for me
In the assemblies of eastern Emain;
There is no peace, nor pleasure, nor repose
In beholding fine houses or splendid ornaments.

What of you, O Conchobur? For me
You have prepared only sorrow under lamentation.
Such will be my life so long as it remains to me;
Your love for me will not last.

≈

[1] *Tindell* is the mother of Noisiu.

THE SONS OF UISLIU

The man who under heaven was fairest to me,
The man who was so dear,
You have torn from me; great was the crime,
So that I shall not see him until I die.

His absence is the cause of grief to me;
The shape of the son of Uisliu shows itself to me,
A dark hill is above his white body,
Which was desired before many things by me.

His ruddy cheeks, more beautiful than meadows,
Red lips, eyebrows the colour of the beetle,
His teeth shining like pearls,
Like the noble color of snow.

Well have I known his splendid garb
Among the warrior men of Alba:
Mantle of crimson, meet for an assembly,
With a border of red gold.

His tunic of satin of costly price,
One hundred pearls upon it, a goodly number;
For its bright embroidery had been used
Fifty ounces of findruine.[2]

A gold-hilted sword in his hand,
Two green spears with terrible points,
A shield with border of yellow gold,
And a boss of silver upon it.

∾

[2] *Findruine* is white bronze.

Fair Fergus brought injury upon us
When inducing us to cross the sea;
He has sold his honour for ale,
The glory of his high deeds is departed.

If there were upon this plain
The warriors of Ulaid in the presence of Conchobur,
all of them would I give up without a struggle
for the companionship of Noisiu, the son of Uisliu.

Break not today my heart (O Conchobur!),
Soon shall I reach my early grave;
Stronger than the sea is my grief,
Dost thou not know it, O Conchobur?

I am Deirdre without joy;
This for me is the end of my life;
Since to remain behind them is the worst thing,
Not long life to myself.

"Whom do you hate the most," said Conchobur, "of these whom you now see?"

"You yourself," she answered, "and with you Eogan mac Durthacht."

"Then," said Conchobur, "you will dwell with Eogan for a year;" and he gave Deirdre over into Eogan's hand.

Now the next day they went away over the festal plain of Macha, and Deirdre sat behind Eogan in the chariot; and the two who were with her were the

A Ewe Between Two Rams

two men whom she would never willingly have seen together upon the earth, and as she looked upon them, "Ha, Deirdre," said Conchobur, "it is the same glance that a ewe gives when between two rams that you share now between me and Eogan!" There was a great rock of stone in front of them, and Deirdre struck her head upon that stone, and she shattered her head, and so she died.

This then is the tale of the exile of the sons of Uisliu, and of the exile of Fergus, and of the death of Deirdre.

Appendix

TRANSLATIONS OF THE NAMES OF THE PLAYERS IN THE HURLEY GAME UPON THE FAIR PLAIN BY LOCH LEIN, WITH SOME NOTES.

O'Grady begins this note-rich section of the text by commenting that some of the heroes are celebrated in Irish mythology but many appear to be fictions of the writer.

∼

Three Garbhs of *Sliabh Mis*. The mountain of Mis (Slieve Mish) in county Kerry.

Three Mases of Sliabh Luachra in county Kerry.

Three yellow-haired Murchadhs.

Three Eochaidhs of *Aine*. The full name is Cnoc Aine; the Hill of Aine in county Limerick. From remote times this hill has been believed to be the residence of Aine, daughter of Eogabhal, of the Tuatha De Danann. She was looked upon as queen of the fairies of south Munster, as Aoibheall of Craglea, near Killaloe, of the fairies of Thomond, or north Munster, and Una of those of Ormond.

Three heroic Laoghaires.

Three Conalls of Collamhan.

Three Fionns of *Fionnmhur*. The white house.

Three Sgals of *Brugh*. This was the Brugh na Boyne.

Three Ronans of *Ath na riogh*. The ford of the rioga (kings), called in English Athenry, a town in county Galway.

Three Eoghans from *Eas ruaidh mhic Bhadhairn*. The cataract of the red one, son of Badharn. The full name of this waterfall is Eas Aodha ruaidh mhic Bhadhairn, the cataract of the red Aodh, son of Badharn; but it is often styled by the Irish writers simply Eas ruaidh, from which the English form Assaroe, now more commonly called the Salmon-leap on the Erne, at Ballyshannon.

Cath-bhuilleach. The battle striker.

Three Fearghuses.

An Glas of *Magh Bhreagh*. The plain of Bregia, which stretches between the Rivers Boyne and Liffey.

An Suirgeach suairc from Lionan. The pleasant or

cheerful wooer.

The Mheidhir from *Beann liath*. Gray peak.

Donn from the *Sidhe Breagh*. There were several Donns in Irish mythology. The mound of Breagh was most probably in the plain of Bregia.

Fear an bheurla bhinn from the Boinn. The man of Sweet Speech from the Boyne.

Colla crionchosach from Bearnan *Eile*. *Colla* means the withered-legged. *Eile* is a district including part of counties Laois and Tipperary.

Donn dumhach. Donn of the sandbanks. This Donn resided at the sandbanks at the mouth of the river Eidhneach, to the west of Ennistymon in county Clare.

Donn an oileain. Donn of the Island.

Donn of Cnoc na n-os. Donn of the Hill of fawns (Knocknanoss in the county of Cork).

Donn of Leinchnoc.

Bruithe *abhac*. The dwarf.

Dolbh the bright-toothed.

Five sons of Fionn *Sidhe Chairn Chaoin*. The mound of the cairn of Caon.

an t-Ilbhreac son of Manannan. The variously-spotted one.

Neamhanach the son of *Aonghus*. Son of Aonghus of the Bruig.

Bodhbh dearg the son of the Deaghdha.

Manannan the son of Lir.

Abhortach the son of *an t-Ioldathach*. Abhortach is the Tuatha De Danann figure considered to be the god or genius of music. *an t-Ioldathach* means the many-colored one.

Fioghmuin of Fionnmhur.

Bibliography

The Pursuit of Diarmuid and Grainne

Toruigheacht Dhiarmuda agus Ghrainne; or, The Pursuit After Diarmuid O'Duibhne, and Grainne the Daughter of Cormac Mac Airt, King of Ireland in the Third Century. Edited by Standish Hayes O'Grady. Dublin: The Ossianic Society, 1857.

Toruigheacht Dhiarmuda agus Ghrainne; The Pursuit of Diarmuid and Grainne. Edited by Standish O'Grady. 2 vol. Dublin: M. H. Gill, 1880-1881.

Toruigheacht Dhiarmuda agus Ghrainne: The Pursuit of Diarmuid and Grainne. New and enlarged edition; re-edited for the Society for the preservation of the Irish language, with notes and a complete vocabulary, by Richard J. O'Duffy. Dublin: M. H. Gill and Son, 1884.

Tóruigheacht Dhiarmada agus Ghráinne: The Pursuit of Diarmaid and Gráinne. Edited by Nessa Ní Shéaghdha. Dublin: The Irish Texts Society, 1967.

Anderson, John Redwood. *The Pursuit of Diarmuid and Graunia*. London: Oxford University Press, 1950.

The Exile of the Sons of Uisliu

Leahy, A. H. *Heroic Romances of Ireland.* 2 vol. London: David Nutt, 1905.

Longes Mac N-Uislenn; The Exile of the Sons of Uisliu. Edited and translated by Vernam Hull. New York: The Modern Language Association of America, 1949.

Longes mac nUsnig: Being the Exile and Death of the Sons of Usnech. Translated by Thomas Kinsella. Dublin: Dolmen Press, 1954.

Oidheadh Chloinne hUisneach; The Violent Death of the Children of Uisneach. Edited and translated by Caoimhín Mac Giolla Léith. London: Irish Texts Society, 1993.

General Bibliography

Breatnach, R. A. "The Pursuit of Diarmaid and Gráinne." *Studies: An Irish Quarterly Review* 47 (1958) 90-97.

Brennan, Charles J. "Some Notes on *The Pursuit of Diarmuid and Grainne.*" *The New Ireland Review* 17 (Mar-Aug, 1902) 55-57.

Candon, Thomas Henry. *The Legend of Diarmuid and Grania: Its History and Treatment by Modern Writers.* Dissertation: Boston University, 1954.

Carson, Ciaran. *The Táin*. London: Penguin Classics, 2008.

Cross, Tom Peete and Clark Harris Slover. *Ancient Irish Tales*. New York: Henry Holt and Co., 1936.

Cunliffe, Barry. *The Ancient Celts*. Oxford: Oxford University Press, 1997.

Dillon, Myles. *Early Irish Literature: An Introduction to the Songs and Legends of Ancient Ireland*. Chicago: University of Chicago Press, 1948.

Dinneen, Patrick S. *Foclóir Gaedilge agus Béarla: an Irish-English Dictionary*. Dublin: The Irish Texts Society, 1927.

Dooley, Ann and Harry Roe. *Tales of the Elders of Ireland*. Oxford: Oxford University Press, 1999.

Gantz, Jeffrey. *Early Irish Myths and Sagas*. London: Penguin, 1981.

Hull, Eleanor. "Old Irish Tabus, or 'Geasa.'" *Folklore* 12.1 (1901) 41-66.

Hull, Eleanor. *A Text Book of Irish Literature*. Parts I-II. Dublin: M. H. Gill & Son, Ltd., n.d.

Hyde, Douglas. *A Literary History of Ireland from Earliest Times to the Present Day*. New edition with introduction by Brian Ó Cuív. London: Ernest Benn Limited, 1899, 1980.

Jackson, Kenneth. *A Celtic Miscellany*. London: Peguin, 1957.

Keating, Geoffrey. *Foras Feasa ar Eirinn: The History of Ireland*. London: The Irish Texts Society, 1902-14.

Kinsella, Thomas. *The Tain*. Oxford: The Oxford University Press, 1970.

McCone, Kim. *Pagan Past and Christian Present in Early Irish Literature*. Maynooth: an Sagart, 1990.

MacCulloch, John Arnott. *Religion of the Ancient Celts*. Edinburgh: T. and T. Clark, 1911.

MacNeill, Eoin et al, ed. *Duanaire Finn: The Book of the Lays of Fionn*. Parts I-III. London: The Irish Texts Society, 1908-53.

Meyer, Kuno. *Fianaigecht*. Royal Irish Academy Todd Lecture Series, vol. XVI. Dublin: Hodges, Figgis & Co., Ltd., 1910; reprinted 1937.

Meyer, Kuno, and Alfred Nutt. *The Voyage of Bran*. 2 vol. London: David Nutt, 1895-97.

Moore, George, and W. B. Yeats. *Diarmuid and Grania; a Three Act Tragedy*. Chicago, De Paul University, 1974.

Murphy, Gerard. *The Ossianic Lore and Romantic Tales of Medieval Ireland*. Dublin: The Cultural Relations Committee of Ireland, 1961.

BIBLIOGRAPHY

O'Curry, Eugene. *Lectures on the MS Materials of Ancient Irish History*. Dublin: James Duffy, 1861.

O'Donovan, John. *Annals of the Four Masters*. Dublin, 1851.

O'Rahilly, Thomas F. *Early Irish History and Mythology*. Dublin: Dublin Institute for Advanced Studies, 1946.

Patterson, Nerys. *Cattle Lords and Clansmen*. Notre Dame: University of Notre Dame Press, 1994.

Reinhard, John R. and Vernam E. Hull. "Bran and Sceolang." *Speculum* 11.1 (1936) 42-58.

"Whortleberry." Horwood, A. R. *British Wild Flowers In Their Natural Haunts*. 6 vol. London: Gresham Publishing Company, 1919.

*This book was designed by Arty Lake for **Old Baldy** Press. Using Adobe InDesign, the text was set in 12 pt minion pro with notes in 10 pt. Printing and binding by Lightning Source.*

Milton Keynes UK
Ingram Content Group UK Ltd.
UKHW021607210324
439908UK00001B/9